HEAVY EQUIPMENT

HEAVY EQU

Erik Bruun and Buzzy Keith

Copyright © 1997, 2004 by Black Dog & Leventhal Publishers, Inc.

All rights reserved. No part of this book may be reproduced
in any form or by any electronic or mechanical means including
information storage and retrieval systems without written
permission of the publisher.

Published by Tess Press, an imprint of
Black Dog & Leventhal Publishers, Inc.
151 West 19th Street, New York, NY 10011

Printed in Italy

Edited by Pamela Horn
Designed by Liz Trovato and Pat Pardini

Front cover photograph © 1996 Joe Baraban

ISBN: 1-57912-410-0

h g f e d c b a

FACING PAGE: *The*
bucket of a hydraulic
excavator.

Tess Press

CONTENTS

CONSTRUCTION EQUIPMENT 16

CRANES 42

Today's combine harvesters make short work of harvesting gigantic tracts of farmland.

Introduction

> "For most purposes, a man with a machine is better than a man without a machine."
>
> HENRY FORD, 1926

This is a book that is meant to impress. The machines described are awe-inspiring. Trucks as big as houses. Shovels as big as buildings with buckets that can hold a six-car garage. Cranes the size of skyscrapers. Giant vehicles that are set into action and guided by signals sent from space. Bulldozers that shove small mountains of earth. And the list goes on, as you will see.

ABOVE: *An Avery Track-Runner tractor was one of hundreds of tractors built in the early part of the twentieth century to mechanize farms.*

Since ancient times when society first started to move earth and materials in earnest, inventors have tried to devise ways to lessen the incredible burden involved. Surely there had to be an easier way to dig a canal than moving a hand-shovel full of dirt at a time, a simpler way to build a pyramid than having teams of farmers and oxen tug 10,000-pound blocks of stone, and a saner way to excavate mines than sending small people into dark and dangerous mines far underground.

Some of the ideas for machines were outrageous for their time. The great Renaissance thinker Leonardo da Vinci was the most famous of a long line of inventive thinkers who put their ideas to paper. The Florentine inventor-artist-engineer came up with proposals to build a crane powered

by a giant treadmill, a dredging excavator that looks very similar to a modern dragline floating on water, and a machine that proved to be a precursor to today's giant bucket wheel excavators. Another Renaissance figure, Giovanni Fontana of Venice, proposed the first known excavator design, although it probably was not built. The proposed excavator was similar to a giant scoop; Fontana anticipated not only future digging machines but also the widespread modern desire of inventors to keep their inventions cloaked in secrecy—the directions for this machine were written in secret code.

The history of machines is a cumulative process, one in which a progressive development of bigger, better, and more effective ways is found to achieve specific objectives. As circumstances change, refinements are made to trim unnecessary pieces of the machine to make its operation more efficient. Parts of the machine are connected in increasingly elabo-

rate ways to maximize the machine's capabilities. As new discoveries are made in engineering, electronics, metal making, computers, and other technologies, they are often applied to all sorts of heavy equipment to make them even more powerful and cost-effective.

After thousands of years of improvements—and with the most dramatic changes occurring during this century—the results are spectacular. Never have machines accomplished so much for so many people. Whether the development of heavy equipment facilitated the growth of a mass society, or the necessities of a mass society spurred the invention of bigger and increasingly more gigantic machines is difficult to say. What is indisputable, however, is that heavy equipment plays a major role in the lives of every person in modern society. Whether people actually ever see a giant bucket wheel excavator, a 60-foot-wide paver, or a million-pound bulldozer or not, they benefit from the work the machines perform whenever they drive over a highway bridge, turn on the heat, or light the coals for an outdoor barbecue.

Giant machines are fascinating. The wonder of a construction site is entrancing to young and old alike, men and women (though usually men), the expert builder and the novice observer. Why, we don't know. Perhaps it speaks to the urge to sculpt the world according to our own desires. People want to build and shape an environment that meets their own criteria of what nature should look like, whether it is building sand castles on the beach as children, tending backyard gardens as adults, or shifting a mountain of earth as an engineer. Heavy equipment fulfills that desire in a way that human muscles cannot. Bulldozers, giant shovels, trenchers, combine harvesters, tower cranes, massive tunnel bores, oil rigs, draglines, bucket wheel excavators, tree chippers give people the power to shove, dig, cut, sort, lift, and move at a scale that only giants could perform. Heavy equipment allows people to be bigger than themselves—in the case of the machines described in this book, a lot bigger.

ABOVE: *A stripping shovel prepares to dump its load onto a giant dump truck in a Rock Springs, Wyoming, coal mine.*

LEFT: *In the early days of heavy equipment, horsepower really was used to make machines such as this harvester work. Note that the mother and daughter have dressed up for the photographer.*

BELOW: *A mechanical digger at work at a construction site in England.*

FACING PAGE, TOP LEFT: *A large dragline unloads a bucketful of coal in an open mine.*

FACING PAGE, BOTTOM LEFT: *A Marion steam shovel lifts a heavy hunk of rock while at work in the Panama Canal at the beginning of the twentieth century.*

FACING PAGE, TOP RIGHT: *A giant mining truck that is too large for public roads.*

FACING PAGE, BOTTOM RIGHT: *No fewer than seven massive cranes are being used for the construction of a nuclear electrical generating plant in San Onofre, California.*

LEFT: *Loosening compacted soil, a tractor pulls a soil cultivator to prepare a field for planting.*

HEAVY EQUIPMENT THROUGH THE AGES

ABOVE: *A nineteenth-century steam shovel on rails digs into the earth. The construction of railroads opened new frontiers in the construction of heavy machinery. Suddenly, there was a pressing need to move massive amounts of earth to make way for trains.*

Aside from relatively primitive cranes in ancient times, the development of heavy equipment as we think of it today did not begin until the Middle Ages when the first excavating machines were invented for dredging rivers, ports, and canals. The need for machines to move and remove materials underwater was the impetus for the first of three major eras in the history of heavy equipment.

Because land transport was uncomfortable, unwieldy, and difficult, waterways served as the primary arteries of communication before the nineteenth century. This meant that work was often required in rivers, canals, and harbors. The simple tools of that era were often not sufficient to even reach, much less excavate, the dirt, rocks, and other materials underwater. Starting in the fifteenth century, medieval inventors began to apply their fertile minds to this problem. The first known excavator design came in about 1420 from Giovanni Fontana of Venice, who proposed a hand-driven floating dredger with a large spoonlike digger to remove dirt on the seafloor surface. It is unclear whether the

machine was built. In the next century, Leonardo da Vinci came up with designs for several similar machines including a crane powered by a treadmill, a canal excavator, and a basket excavator. In fact, in the 1500s, bucket excavators and similar machines powered by people and animals were being built and used to speed the removal of dirt for the construction of canals. By the end of the sixteenth century, at least two types of clamshell excavators were being used in Italian ports.

European inventors came up with a wide variety of excavators and dredges during the next two centuries. But, being powered by either people or animals, the machines were limited by the strength and endurance of the creatures' muscles. In 1742, however, the Frenchman Martin Peltier invented the first wind-powered excavator, a massive 100-foot machine whose 40-foot bucketwheel removed 40 cubic yards of sand an hour. In 1765, the Scottish inventor and engineer James Watt invented the modern condensing steam engine, unleashing a new mechanical force to drive machines. Although the steam engine was initially used for stationary

LEFT: *The size of shovels increased exponentially in the twentieth century. Here a large stripping shovel removes overburden from a coal mine, while a significantly smaller one loads the exposed coal onto a hauling truck.*

ABOVE: *A wheeled steam shovel builds a road in 1914. Horses and engine-driven machines worked together for many years before mechanization prevailed.*

FACING PAGE, TOP: *Though historically dubious, this illustration of Noah and his workers building an ark does convey the toil of using hand tools in ancient times to build large objects.*

machines, it did not take long for engineers to use its force to power a wide range of steam excavators, dredges, and bucket-wheel-type machines. Almost all of the equipment prior to the 1830s was applied to water uses, and in part that explains the explosion of canal construction in the United States in the early part of the nineteenth century.

The invention of the railroad in 1830, however, changed all of that and cleared the way for the second great epoch in excavating machinery. Railroads increased the scale of earthmoving projects to a new level. Tens of thousands of rail lines were built in the United States and Europe from 1830 to 1900. The driving demand was beyond the capacity of the equipment and tools used for earth-moving up to that time. William Otis's power shovel invented in the 1830s was the first modern excavator. Not coincidentally, it was built to save labor in the construction of rail-road lines. Able to move 500 cubic yards of earth a day, the steam shovel could replace between 50 and 120 workers a day. The nineteenth century saw a rapid growth in the number and size of power shovels, bucket excavators, and clamshells— mounted on rail lines, powered by steam engines and then by diesel engines—whose primary purpose was to make way for the railroad.

The third and final shift in heavy equipment occurred at the end of the nineteenth century with the development of gasoline engines and mobile machines no longer dependent on steel tracks. The need for roads meant that large numbers of new and improved types of equipment were used for the construction of motorways, which in turn helped create the mass society that has pushed the size of machines to greater and greater scales.

ABOVE, CENTER: *Two trucks and a shovel, all petite and primitive by contemporary standards, build a country road.*

LEFT: *At the turn of the twentieth century the transition from animal power to mechanized power was fully under way. Here, three steam-rollers and their crews take a break as teams of horses look on.*

GIANT ANCI

Ancient history is replete with mammoth earthmoving ventures, even by today's gargantuan standards. Instead of massive engines, reinforced steel, and automated equipment, ancient builders relied on ingenuity, blood, and sweat to accomplish their tasks. Applying basic engineering techniques to create simple machines, they were able to accomplish astounding feats. In many ways, projects such as the Great Wall of China, the Egyptian pyramids, and the Inca roads are even more impressive when you consider the simplicity of the tools used and the fact that the power was derived almost exclusively from human and animal muscle. It takes eight workers with pick axes, shovels, and baskets on their backs a full day to move 20 cubic yards of dirt 200 yards. A single motorized scraper today will accomplish the same job in less than 2 minutes. The amount of toil and persistence it took for workers from pre-industrial times to complete their projects is just as impressive, if not more so, than the largest strip-mining shovels, giant dump trucks, and other machinery of today.

The greatest earthmoving project of antiquity was the construction of the Egyptian pyramids. For 1,000 years, when pharaohs or their queens died, their mummified bodies were placed in pyramids of varying sizes. The Great Pyramid at Giza is the largest of all pyramids. Built for King Khufu and completed in about 2565 B.C., the structure consists of 2 million blocks of stone weighing up to 15 tons each. It is 485 feet high and 755 feet wide at the base, giving it an original volume of more 110 million cubic feet and a weight of more than 6 million tons. When Napoleon Bonaparte, while on a military expedition, saw the pyramid in 1798 he told his general that the mass of stone was enough to build a wall 1 foot wide and 9 feet high round the whole of France, a calculation that proved to be surprisingly accurate. Free Egyptians built the Great Pyramid and the other pyramids as an act of worship to their kings. Stone, which was typically cut in 2½-ton blocks, was quarried and brought to Giza first by boat and then dragged from the Nile River by sleds. Using ramps and simple cranes, workers maneuvered the stones into

ABOVE: Even by contemporary standards, the construction of the Great Pyramids in Egypt was a monumental undertaking. Unlike today, however, workers did not have the benefit of modern machinery to build these mammoth edifices. This view from the air is of the Great Pyramid of Khufu.

TOP: The Great Wall of China has stood the test of time as one of the great construction projects in all history. Like the pyramids, thousands of workers used very simple tools to complete the task.

place one at a time. Archaeologists estimate it took 20 years to build the Great Pyramid.

All Roads Lead to Rome.

Although many ancient societies built roads, Rome can justifiably claim credit for developing the first comprehensive network of roads. Starting in the fourth century B.C., Rome began to build a great highway system that eventually embraced Italy, France, Spain, Germany, eastern Europe, England, the Middle East, and northern Africa. If combined, the roads would be long enough to circle the equator twice. Trade, communications, and military reasons all prompted the growing empire to build the roads. Improvements in road construction such as the development of lime mortar in 300 B.C. and natural cement in 150 B.C. quickened the pace of road building. Generally speaking, Roman roads consisted of four layers: an 8- to 12-inch mortar layer on top of sand course, a 12- to 18-inch-thick layer of blocks in cement mortar, a 12-inch slab of concrete with crushed stone, and finally a top layer consisting of 8 to 16 inches of stone or gravel concrete. The roads, which were typically about 40 feet wide, had drainage ditches on either side and were cleared of brush. The Roman crane, a simple, but highly effective tool for a wide assortment of construction projects, including bridges, aqueducts, buildings, and coliseums, was used for road construction projects by workers, who were often soldiers, gladiators, slaves, or local farmers.

Other major earthmoving projects from ancient times include the building of Mount Knocknaraea in Ireland, a 30,000-cubic-yard, human-made summit built to honor God; a 1,000-mile canal linking Peking with Hanshou; a 400-foot-long, 300-foot-wide dam in Egypt; and the Great Wall of China. Although China would later be on the cutting edge of excavation machinery, to build the Great Wall the emperor Shih Huang Ti relied more on brute force than ingenuity. Tens of thousands of workers were forced to build the mammoth 1,500-mile-long, 30-foot-high wall along the northern border of China. Many of the workers were worked to death and buried where they fell inside the wall.

Left: The Great Wall of China was built more than 2,000 years ago. Stretching 1,500 miles along the northern Chinese frontier, the wall provided protection from marauding tribes to the north.

Right: Rome's highway system connected all corners of its empire throughout Europe, northern Africa, and the Middle East. Engineers and work crews did a significant amount of preliminary work for the road, including construction of drainage systems and subsurface preparation to make sure the roads would remain intact. This road goes over the Sierra de Gredos, a mountain range in Spain.

Above: The Emperor Shih Huang Ti relentlessly pushed workers to complete the Great Wall of China. When someone collapsed on the job, which was a frequent occurrence, he was often left to die while his companions built the wall over him. Thousands of workers are believed to be buried inside the 30-foot-high wall.

Right: Using soldiers, slaves, and other workers, Rome built an extraordinary network of roads and streets. This stone road in Pompeii, Italy, was built to last as it still remains virtually the same as when it was first constructed.

LEFT: *In one of the great historic photographs of men and machinery United States president Theodore Roosevelt sits in engineer A. H. Grey's driver's seat on a 95-ton Bucyrus-Erie shovel, the mainstay of the Panama Canal project. In addition to the engineer, the shovel's 10-man crew consisted of two coal stokers, a craneman to handle the dumping, and a six-man "move-up" crew that positioned the shovel.*

▲ An estimated 61 million pounds of dynamite was used at the Culebra Cut, more explosive energy than had previously been consumed in all United States' wars.

A dredge works to clean up a mud slide in the Culebra Cut. The project suffered countless setbacks because of mud slides in the tropical conditions, accounting for almost a third of the total amount of earth removed in the project. Note the bucket wheel excavator in the rear. The French had relied heavily on bucket wheel excavators 20 years earlier, but the machines were not up to the mammoth task.

PANAMA CANAL

To this day the Panama Canal is the only water route through the American continental land mass. Its locks continue to serve a crucial role in world commerce nearly a century after the gigantic project was completed.

▲ The amount of earth removed to make way for the Panama Canal would fill a line of railroad cars stretched around the world at the equator four times.

Completed in 1914, the digging of the Panama Canal was the single largest construction project in world history up to that time, and aside from the waging of war, the most expensive undertaking in United States history.

All told, more than 360 million cubic yards of earth were excavated. By contemporary mining standards this may not sound like an extraordinary feat. But at the turn of the twentieth century, in the midst of a sweltering, disease-infested tropical jungle, using shovels with a top capacity of 5 cubic yards to remove a mountain of solid rock, it was, as the British jurist, historian, and diplomat Lord Bryce noted, the greatest liberty ever taken with nature.

Prior to the canal, more than a hundred proposals had been put forth to link the Atlantic and Pacific Oceans with a canal piercing Central America. In the 1880s, the French attempted to build such a canal through Panama, at that time a part of Columbia. The builder of the Suez Canal, Ferdinand de Lesseps, oversaw the project, which made significant headway before bankruptcy, scandal, disease, and insufficient equipment brought the undertaking to an unseemly conclusion.

Undaunted by the French failure and invigorated by the possibility of linking the two oceans, the United States took up the cause. With the help of the military pressure on Columbia, Panama seceded from Colombia in 1903 in a bloodless revolution, thus setting the stage for the United States to build the canal under favorable conditions. Digging commenced in 1907 and went forward without pause until the canal opened in 1914.

Far and away the most daunting aspect of the canal was the Culebra Cut, a 9-mile ditch excavated out of a small mountain. Every morning 6,000 workers entered the giant ditch to blast, dig, and haul. More than 300 jackhammers were in use at any given moment. In a typical month, 800,000 sticks of dynamite were laid into holes that if stretched out would in aggregate be 65 miles deep. Accidents were commonplace, prompting one worker to recall, "The flesh of men flew in the air like birds many days."

The mainstay was a 95-ton Bucyrus shovel. Equipped with a 5-cubic-yard bucket that could lift 8 tons of earth, its capacity was three times greater than any machines used by the French in the first effort. Mounted on a railroad car, it required ten men to operate, including an engineer, craneman, two coal stokers, and a six-man crew that shifted its track. At the project's peak, 68 shovels were in operation in the cut removing 2 million cubic yards a month. The local newspaper reported on each shovel's progress. Shovel No. 123 set the project record, removing 70,000 cubic yards of earth in 26 days. A single shovel could fill a railroad car in eight minutes, which would then be hauled as far as 26 miles to be dumped.

Beyond the Culebra Cut, engineers had to build entire sewer systems, new water supplies, and douse and fill mosquito-infested swamps to rid the region of malaria and yellow fever, which had killed 5 percent of the workers a year when the French had attempted to build the canal. The project also included the construction of the half-mile-wide, 107-foot-high Gatun Dam and the development of a network of colossal concrete-lined canal locks. Each lock was six stories high and 1,000 feet long. The canal doors, which were as much as 6 feet thick, were operated by 1,500 motors designed and built by General Electric, a small up-and-coming company that had taken on the venture as its first government contract.

When the project was completed, the United States had spent $350 million, or four times the amount expended to acquire all of the country's terrain and overseas possessions since the American Revolution, including the Louisiana Purchase, Florida, California, Alaska, and the Philippines. More than 5,500 lives had been lost to disease and accidents under the United States' direction, on top of an estimated 20,000 deaths in the first attempt. Despite the obstacles, unforeseen landslides, disease, and the sheer size of the project, in the end it came in $23 million under budget and was opened six months ahead of schedule.

The world's largest earth-moving venture at the dawn of the twenty-first century is the massive and controversial Three Gorges Dam project on the Chang Jiang, or Yangtze River, in China. When completed, the dam will be 1.3 miles long and 610 feet high, which is to say it will be taller than a 60-story building extended 30 city blocks or six times longer than the Hoover Dam in the United States. The resulting reservoir will be 375 miles long, or as long as Lake Superior, and contain 36 billion cubic yards of water.

Twenty-six sets of 700-megawatt turbines and generators will provide 18,200 megawatts of electricity. The dam, which is slated to be completed by the Chinese government in 2009, will generate half again as much power as the world's current largest energy-producing power station at the Itaipu Dam in Brazil. It will also include a five-step canal for ships as large as 10,000 tons to pass through. The Chinese government also hopes that the dam will provide flood protection for downstream sections of central and eastern China. The Yangtze Valley has been plagued with devastating floods throughout its history. A 1954 flood left nearly 20 million people homeless and 30,000 people dead.

Like the other gigantic human-made Chinese venture, the Great Wall of China, Three Gorges Dam will be visible from the moon with a telescope and will represent the country's capacity to build giant projects through sheer force of numbers. More than 40,000 workers have been blasting and digging at the massive construction site to build the structure since Li Peng, then premier of China, poured the first concrete for the dam just upstream from Sandouping. Thousands of over-size trucks, bulldozers, shovels, and cranes are being employed for Three Gorges Dam, which is named after the Qutang, Wu and Xiling gorges along the Yangtze Valley. The cost and complications of the project vary wildly. The official estimate is that it will cost $12 billion to complete the project on time. Other estimates project the cost at $75 billion or more, with a ten year schedule overrun. So, how much equipment, the number of people, the final cost, and whether it will even be completed are open questions.

Among other issues, the project involves the relocation of more than 1.2 million people living in the 62,000 acres of land that will be submerged underwater when the dam is completed. This area, which is in the process of being evacuated, includes 13 cities, 140 towns, hundreds of villages, 300,000 farmers, and more than 1,000 significant historical and archaeological sites dating back 10,000 years. Aside from the highly charged issue of relocating so many people are questions concerning the safety of the project, its feasibility, and the environmental impact. Critics charge that the dam is being built on a seismic fault line, making the structure vulnerable to earthquakes. If the dam were to break, up to 400,000 cubic yards of water per second would descend on 10 million people downstream. Further, they say that sedimentation in the river will wreak havoc with the dam if it is ever completed.

Environmentalists vehemently oppose the project for the destruction it will cause in the submerged areas and because of concerns that the water will be contaminated by hundreds of toxic dumps and other polluted sites, causing a long-term pollution problem for the entire river. The weight of these and other concerns influenced the World Bank to reject taking part in the financing of the project; the Chinese government is raising the money on its own. Efforts to raise the money through private international financing have also stumbled.

Thus, the Three Gorges Dam project is not only the largest earthmoving project ever undertaken, it is also an extreme example and emblematic of the issues that confront almost all large-scale development: how to meet the growing energy, transportation and consumption needs of a modern mass society and at the same time pay for it, protect the environment, and avoid trampling on people's rights in an increasingly crowded world.

Below, left: *China has not employed many giant pieces of equipment for the Three Gorges Dam project to date. Instead, they have relied on large numbers of equipment and workers. When it is completed, the dam is expected to provide 18,200 megawatts of electricity and include a five-step canal for large ships to navigate.*

▲ Estimated costs for the project have soared from $4.5 billion in 1986 to more than $75 billion. About 40,000 workers using trucks, shovels, and cranes have been working on the project since 1995. The Chinese government expects to complete the project (which entails building a dam the height of a 60-story building stretched for 1.3 miles) in 2009

THE THREE GORGES DAM

A ferry makes its way through the scenic Three Gorges Dam Area on the Yangtze River. Environmentalists have vigorously opposed the construction of the project, for it will result in the flooding of 62,000 acres, including 13 cities, 140 towns, and hundreds of villages, many of which have badly contaminated industrial sites. Critics of the project also contend that the dam may be unsafe because of its vulnerability to earthquakes and the excessive amount of silt in the Yangtze River.

Top, right: The Three Gorges Dam project in China is the world's largest construction project. More than 40,000 workers are helping to build the 1.3-mile-long dam across the Yangtze River. The project is expected to be completed by about 2010.

Bottom, right: The Chinese government estimates the gigantic project will cost $12 billion to complete, although other estimates place the final price tag upwards of $75 billion. When completed, the dam will be the same height as a 60-story building and as long as 30 city blocks.

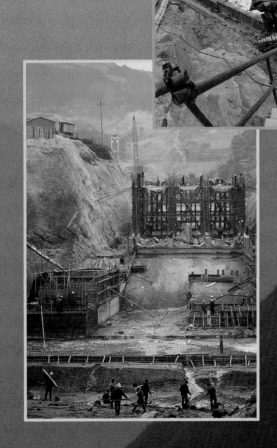

When completed, Three Gorges Dam will create a 385-mile-long reservoir, elevate the Yangtze's water level by 285 feet (or the height of a 25-story building), and produce 18,200 megawatts of electricity. It will also submerge 115,000 acres of farmland, 13 cities, hundreds of towns and villages, and the homes of more than 1.2 million people.

CONSTRUCTION EQUIPMENT

The vast majority of heavy equipment is used for construction. Whether it is roads, houses, shopping complexes, landfills, buildings, subdivisions, dams, tunnels, or any other construction project, heavy equipment is sure to be on-site. Heavy equipment has relieved most of the human burden of building. Cold steel has replaced aching muscles. Less than a century old, modern construction equipment has built cities and nations. Bulldozers, excavators, front-end loaders, scarpers, graders, and many other machines have literally changed the face of the earth in many parts of the world.

Properly used, construction equipment is a wonder to behold in action. Snorting and grinding their way around a construction site, the machines seem to dance with one another, working in conjunction to build a new entity. To the untrained eye, it may look like a mess—a mass of metal and rubber scurrying about, digging, moving, pushing, carrying, and lifting whatever is in the way—but it is fascinating. The captivation of construction equipment—especially for boys—starts at an early age, and for many it never ends.

ROAD CONSTRUCTION AND HIGHWAY EQUIPMENT

Road construction, by and large, does not require gigantic equipment. Most roads are relatively narrow ribbons of asphalt whose economies of scale do not justify or require the expense of gigantic machinery. Nevertheless, road construction accounts for perhaps the single largest hunk of work carried out by heavy machinery and is certainly the most visible use of construction equipment.

With more than 3.9 million miles of road in the United States alone, billions of dollars are spent every year on the maintenance and construction of roads and highways.

Building a road is an equipment-intensive activity. A minimum of seven pieces of heavy machinery, costing about $200,000 each, are needed to build a typical road, from preparing the ground to laying the asphalt. Several other pieces of heavy equipment are then needed for proper maintenance. Creativity is one of the hallmarks of most of the equipment. Though the equipment has one primary purpose, innovative designers and operators have frequently found a host of secondary uses for almost all of the following equipment:

Bulldozer

Usually the first piece of equipment on a highway construction project, the bulldozer serves the role of the demolition man. Like a heavily armed mechanical gladiator, a bulldozer bears a blade on its front specifically for the purpose of moving earth and almost anything else that may get in its way. The front blade, called a *dozer*, pushes the earth, grass, bushes, and trees to lay the ground for a road. A knifelike attachment on the rear called a *ripper* is jammed into the ground and dragged by the bulldozer to rip the compacted earth rocks, and roots below. Cost of a typical bulldozer: $180,000.

Scraper

A scraper is a mechanized shovel/wheelbarrel that cuts the earth, carries it to another destination, dumps it, and returns to repeat the process over and over again. The front portion of a scraper is the tractor, where the operator and controls are located. The back portion is the *scraper* where the bowl, or *can*, is located to hold the dirt. The cutting edge of the bowl has pieces of metal attached to it called *slobber bits* that cut the earth when the bowl is lowered to the ground while the scraper is moving. There are other types of scrapers with a second engine in the rear and various dirt-loading systems. Cost of a typical scraper: $250,000.

Grader

When the rough layout of a road is completed, the grader applies the finishing touches to the road's earthen foundation before the asphalt is added. Usually 26 to 32 feet long, the grader's skeletal frame carries a blade underneath its body. The blade, or *moldboard*, can be adjusted to sculpt the ground below. Working with compactors, graders create smooth pathways and provide a solid base from which to builds roads. Cost of a typical grader: $175,000.

Excavator

Originally known as steam shovels, excavators do the heavy digging required in preparing the groundwork of a road. Buckets ranging in size from 0.5 to over 10.5 cubic yards dangle from a metal arm to do the digging. The digging arm, consisting of a *boom* and *stick*, can stretch as long as 60 feet. While digging is usually its principal job, excavators are also often used to uproot trees, lay down piping, and to perform a wide variety of other tasks, sometimes using specialized accessory equipment in place of the buckets. It is only a slight exaggeration to say that a skilled operator can do everything from lifting a gigantic boulder to parting the hair of a colleague. Cost of a typical excavator: $200,000.

Asphalt Compactors

After the asphalt is applied, three different types of finish compactors mash the hot asphalt into a compressed mass suitable for traffic. The first one is a breakdown roller that breaks down and compacts the asphalt with two steel drums equipped with vibratory mechanisms that can double the effective weight of the roller. The first pass, known as *pinching the joint*, is followed by another roller with nine heavy pneumatic rubber tires that seal and further compact the asphalt. The final compacting is done by the finish roller, a compactor with two smooth, nonvibrating steel rollers that seal the surface. Cost of a typical asphalt compactor: $125,000.

Paver

The paver distributes the hot mix of asphalt (the temperature of the mix has to be between 250 and 375 degrees Fahrenheit) on to the road base. With widths ranging from 4 to 40 feet, pavers lay out an asphalt spread that is usually between 4 and 12 inches thick. A *hopper* holds the asphalt and is frequently reloaded with fresh supplies of hot asphalt. Driven by a single operator, pavers are usually accompanied by at least two workers on foot known as *screed men* who constantly measure the asphalt's depth and temperature. Going at a speed of 60 to 150 feet per minute, consistency—not speed—is the priority for pavers. Cost of a typical paver: $250,000.

Wheeled Compactor

Seemingly straightforward machines, compactors (also known as *rollers*) come in different varieties. The first type has a vibrating steel drum in the front and wheels in the rear. The steel drum can either be smooth, for compaction of sand and other granular materials, or have protusions similar to giant goose bumps, which are called *padfoot drums*, for clay-type soils. The second type has four padfoot drums at each corner and a blade in the front. It is designed where high volumes of compaction are required. Cost of a typical compactor: $100,000.

Bulldozers

Farm fields, landfills, highway construction sites, mining pits, blazing forest fires, building sites, and even battlefields. These are just some of the places you may find a bulldozer, among the most versatile and yet simplest of heavy machines.

The concept of a bulldozer is straightforward: Take a heavy, slightly curved plate of metal, place a strong engine on tracks behind, it and push. The term *bulldozer* has its roots in the nineteenth century, long before anyone even imagined today's powerful machines. To *bull-doze*, first used in 1876, meant to bully or intimidate a person to get one's way. A type of large pistol was given the name *bulldozer* in the 1880s mainly because of its intimidation value.

It was not until the 1930s that the term was commonly used for what we today think of as bulldozers, or *dozers*. Up until then the machines were called track-type tractors or crawlers, which were basically tractors with steel blades attached in front for pushing dirt.

In their early days, crawlers were very simple and very heavy but lacked the horsepower that diesel engines would start to provide in the 1930s. Nevertheless, they fired the imagination even then.

The effectiveness of crawler tractors in the United States inspired the British military to invent the tank during World War I. Lieutenant Colonel Ernest Swinton, considered the father of the modern tank, described the Holt Manufacturing Company's Caterpillar crawler tractor factory as the "the cradle of the tank." While bulldozers have played a role in the military ever since, including a prominent one in the Persian Gulf War of 1991, their primary role has been for less bellicose purposes.

The advent of more powerful engines and the ingenuity of engineers have spurred the development of bigger machines with a more diverse selection of implements. Most large bulldozers have rippers attached to their rear; these large knifelike pieces of metal are inserted into the ground and pulled through the earth causing dirt, stumps, rocks, and anything else in their path to be loosened or ripped out. Dozer blades have been designed for a variety of purposes ranging from sculpting the landscape to shielding operators from oil-

ABOVE: *Two Caterpillar bulldozers plow their way through an Atlanta, Georgia, construction site. Note the elevated sprocket design in the crawler. Caterpillar developed the innovation in 1978 to improve the machine's stability.*

LEFT: *A special blade is used by bulldozers to catch and hold stray debris when working in landfills.*

ABOVE: *A bulldozer blade clears a path in the construction of Route 394 in Minnesota.*

well fires. With slight modifications or the addition of attachments, bulldozers are used to extinguish fires, push rocks, sweep agricultural fields of stumps, manage landfills, and build stockpiles.

Most bulldozers today are used for construction, however, where they prepare the groundwork for buildings or roadways. Moving earth is what bulldozers were originally designed for and it is still how they are most commonly used.

Bulldozers range in size from small (less than 100 horsepower) to immense (the world's largest is the Komatsu 575A-2 with a 1,050-horsepower engine). Generally speaking, larger bulldozers last longer than smaller ones. According to Equipment Data Associates, the majority of the close 120,000 bullldozers in the United States are owned by construction companies. Mining companies, however, get the most use of their bulldozers, operating them an average of 2,700 hours a year or more, better than twice the average use by construction companies and almost four times the average use by government-owned bulldozers.

ABOVE: *Bulldozers can be found all over the world doing all sorts of things. This bulldozer is helping to move timber in Costa Rica.*

⚠ The Caterpillar D11N is the largest bulldozer made in the United States. It weighs 215,000 pounds and is powered by a 770-horsepower V-8 engine.

Komatsu D575A-2 Super Dozer

When the Komatsu D575A-2 Super Dozer was introduced in 1996, it nearly doubled the production capacity of the largest bulldozers. Weighing in at well over 300,000 pounds, powered by a 1,150-horsepower engine, and equipped with a wide array of new technologies for bulldozers, the D575A-2 can move 90 cubic yards of dirt and rip gigantic boulders out of the ground.

The Super Dozer's blade is almost 11 feet high and up to 25 feet wide, giving it the approximate dimensions of a highway billboard. The vehicle is 16 feet tall, 25 feet wide, and depending on whether a counterweight is included, up to 38 1/2 feet long. This means that it is about as big as a two-bedroom house. The fuel tank holds 555 gallons of diesel and the radiator 78 gallons of water. The machine holds as much as 79 gallons of hydraulic oil and 34 gallons of oil

to lubricate the 12-piston engine. The Super Dozer travels up to 8 miles per hour.

Typically used for mines and the reclamation of mines, the Super Dozer was the result of 12 years and millions of dollars of research. Some of the innovations include a hull-type frame that provides improved strength with less mass than the conventional I-beam rail construction, track rollers mounted on X-type bogies with rubber pads that absorb ground shock and allow the machine to hug the contour of the ground, and the use of five planetary gears in the final drive to lengthen the machine's durability. In addition, Komatsu designed it to have a low center of gravity and extralong crawlers, thus providing for extra strength, stability and traction. Each crawler is 18 feet long, almost 3 feet wide, and consists of forty-nine 4-inch thick shoes. The ground contact area is 14,623 square inches, making the

ground pressure a relatively modest 21 1/2 pounds per square inch.

The driver of a D575A-2 Super Dozer sits in a cab with air-conditioning, heating, and panoramic tinted glass that is mounted on a rubber shock absorbers to soften the ride. All meters and gauges are backlit with liquid-crystal displays. A joystick controls all blade movements. Brakes are applied with both a lever and pedal, and the steering clutches are controlled with a lever. A monitoring system keeps tab of the condition of the machine's various components.

ABOVE: *The Komatsu D575A-2 Super Dozer is the world's largest bulldozer, capable of moving 90 cubic yards of dirt (enough to fill three large Dumpster trash containers) with a single shove. Its blade has the approximate dimensions of a highway billboard.*

The typical job of a scraper on a road construction project involves removing a layer of dirt, storing it in its bowl in the rear, hauling it to a nearby location, and then dumping the load.

Heft is usually what is most prized in heavy equipment. But with scrapers speed and efficiency are the priorities. A cross between a shovel and hauler, scrapers load, haul, dump, and spread earth in an almost seamless cycle. A scraper's primary function is to move earth from one place to another.

In short hauls of less than 500 feet, scrapers compete with bulldozers as the most efficient machinery for the task. For longer distances of 2,000 feet or more, a combination of a loader and hauler is likely to be more efficient.

Developed in the 1950s, motorized scrapers literally scrape the earth with a blade or elevating system that forces the dirt into a *bowl.* The depth varies between 3 or 4 inches to a foot. The bowl is typically about 20 cubic yards, but can be as large as 44 cubic yards. Having collected its load, the scraper lifts the bowl, drives to its destination, and disgorges its contents.

The advantage of a scraper is that it picks up and unloads materials very efficiently. The disadvantage is that the operating expense is high for moving materials long distances, especially when compared with loader-truck combinations. Scrapers are typically used for moving

▲ The largest scraper ever built was LeTourneau's LT-360, known as the "Electric Digger." It consisted of three scrapers joined together by links. Close to 200 feet long, each container could hold 120 tons. Its eight engines totaled 5,080 horsepower, giving the machine enough power to load each container in less than 30 seconds.

The challenge for standard scrapers is generating enough horsepower to scoop the earth into its bowls. Bulldozers are frequently employed to meet this shortcoming, particularly when the ground is very hard.

This Caterpillar scraper shows the two main components of a scraper. The tractor provides the power to move the machine, while the bowl in the rear holds the material that is being hauled.

Scrapers

earth on road construction sites and dams, stripping topsoil, contour grading, or preparing building sites.

There are three basic types of scrapers. The standard scraper has a single-engine tractor that pulls an open bowl. In most cases, the tractor does not have enough power to load significant amounts of soil without assistance from a bulldozer. All scrapers have an extended rear section that allows a bulldozer blade to push against it to assist in loading or when the unit gets stuck.

Twin-engine scrapers avoid the need for a bulldozer engine in many cases by adding a second source of power in the rear of the machine. Although bulldozers can still be used to assist twin-engine scrapers, it is more common for two twin-engine scrapers to supplement each other's power in what is called a push-pull arrangement. While one of the scrapers lowers its bowl to pick up the dirt, the other scraper connects itself to an attachment and helps push. After the first unit is loaded, the scrapers reverse roles—the second unit picks up the dirt while the first machine does the pushing.

An elevating scraper avoids the need of a

bulldozer; it has a self-loading system in the front of the bowl that digs and scoops the dirt with an elevator mechanism that loads the bowl. Elevating scrapers, however, do not handle rocks or hard soil very well, and they have higher operating costs.

ABOVE: *Two scrapers working in tandem.*

RIGHT: *Scrapers frequently supplement each other's power in a push-pull arrangement in which one scraper helps push or pull the other as it scrapes the earth, and then the two switch tasks.*

BELOW: *Elevating scrapers, such as this Caterpillar 633E, have a self-loading system in which a mechanism at the front of the bowl lifts the material onto the bowl. This is the largest in Caterpillar's line with a 475-horsepower engine and a 34-cubic-yard bowl capacity.*

▲ Caterpillar manufactures the largest scraper, a Caterpillar 657E. A twin-engine scraper, it has a 44-cubic-yard bowl and a 950-horsepower engine. Caterpillar dominates the scraper industry. Well over half of the scrapers in operation in the United States are built by the heavy equipment manufacturer.

Front-end Loaders

A front-end loader doing what it does best: lifting and removing dirt.

BELOW: *A bucket dumps its load of aggregate material in a port.*

▲ The most common loaders range from a 1-cubic-yard bucket with a 60- to 80-horsepower engine to a 8- or 9-cubic-yard bucket with a 700-horse-power engine that will hold 50,000 pounds or more. Some companies such as Marathon Le Tourneau and Dresser manufacture loaders with buckets that exceed 30 cubic yards and can hold more than 150,000 pounds of material.

Front-end loaders are very useful, multipurpose machines, serving the role of both the fixed-position excavator and a transporter over short distances. Equipped in the front with a bucket the width of the machine, front-end loaders are primarily designed to excavate soil, rock, debris, and other materials; lift this load to the desired location (usually into a truck or to a stockpile); and then dump the materials.

There are two general categories of loaders: those with wheels and those with tracks. Wheeled loaders are the most popular with sizes ranging from small 1-cubic-yard buckets to the giant machines weighing almost 250 tons with 33-cubic-yard-capacity buckets.

Crawler loaders are found where traction and tight maneuverability are needed. Sizes generally do not exceed a capacity for 25 tons.

Originally operated with mechanical arms, the development of hydraulics in the late 1960s increased the bucket capacity, machine speed, and efficiency of loaders. A typical task for a loader is loading a pile of debris onto a dump truck. The constant digging and lifting of materials, combined with the back-and-forth of the machine to perform this chore can require 400 to 500 direction changes per hour, meaning that operating a loader can be a very taxing job.

Depending on the task, different buckets can be used for loaders. The most common type of bucket is a general purpose bucket for dirt and small-rock excavation. It has a thick metal plate, steel teeth and a concave bucket, all of which allow the machine to dig, lift, and haul with relative ease. Next in popularity is the space nose bucket for large rocks and tough digging. Other buckets are the multipurpose which allows for discharge of the material from the front or bottom of the bucket, and the side-dump bucket, which discharges the material to the right or left. Other attachments that can be installed in place of a bucket are forks, rakes, and brooms.

The addition of backhoes onto the rear of loaders adds to their versatility. These small digging attachments are powered by the loader's engine and are operated from separate controls in the rear section of the machine. These backhoe attachments can execute smaller tasks such as digging trenches and holes and can reach areas that the front bucket can't. Many crawler loaders have rippers mounted on the rear to dislodge small rocks and to break up hard compacted soil.

Because of the wide variety of attachments available for the front and rear of loaders, each can be customized for a specific job assignment. Loaders are found on almost all construction sites and are the second-most versatile machine on a job site, after the excavator.

LEFT: *Scooping a load of coal, this front-end loader is being used for stockpiling purposes.*

ABOVE: *Front-end loaders are among the more versatile pieces of machinery, capable of both hauling and excavating. This one is at work in a biomass energy plant.*

LEFT: *A giant front-end loader at work in a Kansas coal mine. Note the reinforced tires to provide extra traction.*

Graders

▲ Like other categories of heavy equipment, the largest greders are used for mining. Caterpillar's 24H Mining Motor Grader weighs 65 tons, has a 500-horsepower engine, and carries a 24-foot moldboard wide enough to cover two highway lanes.

ABOVE: *The Caterpillar 24H Mining Motor Grader is the largest grader made today. Its moldboard is up to 24 feet long, or wide enough to grade more than two highway lanes at a time.*

LEFT: *Self-propelled graders were first built in the 1920s. They were essentially modified tractors with blades placed underneath the driver's seat. This one grades a Florida road in the 1930s.*

Even before there were automobiles, there were graders. Drawn by horses, graders smoothed the trails and primitive roads of the pre-automobile era. With the invention of cars, however, graders became one of the most important pieces of machinery in the construction of roads.

Initially, track-type tractors simply replaced horses. With the grader attached to the tractor's rear, its blade leveled the earth as the tracked machine pulled it forward. This proved to be a very effective and economical way to build the first roads for cars.

Before long new self-propelled graders were being developed, particularly by the Russell Grader Manufacturing Company. The new graders were modified tractors with blades suspended below to carve and smooth the earth below.

In 1931, Caterpillar introduced the Auto Patrol. Marked by several innovations, many consider it to be the first true motor grader. Its engine was placed high and in the rear to improve visibility for the operator, and pneumatic tires allowed the machine to travel at greater speeds.

Although several improvements have been made to enhance the comfort, speed, efficiency, and economics of graders, they have remained fundamentally the same since then.

Usually 26 to 32 feet long, the grader's skeletal frame carries a blade underneath its body. The blade, or *moldboard*, can be adjusted side to side and up and down and can be rotated 225 degrees to sculpt the ground below. Working with compactors, graders create smooth pathways and provide a solid base from which to build roads.

The largest graders are used for building and maintaining mining roads, for reclaimation projects, and for other large-scale duties. The Caterpillar 24H motor grader, for example, is more than twice the size of the standard grader used in road construction. It weighs 130,000 pounds, has a 500-horsepower engine, and carries a 20- or 24-foot-long, 3 1/2-foot-high moldboard.

LEFT: *The first graders were attachments dragged by tractors. They frequently needed a second operator to control the blade.*

BELOW: *This John Deere grader has a laser unit mounted to the grader blade that allows the machine to sculpt the earth to precise measurements.*

BOTTOM: *View from the inside of a Caterpillar 24H Mining Motor Grader.*

▲ The modern grader was invented in 1919 by the Russell Grader Manufacturing Company. The machine, initially called the Motor Hi-Way Patrol, was a converted two-wheel Allis-Chalmers tractor on steel wheels with a blade suspended beneath the driver's seat. Caterpillar bought the company in 1928 and has dominated the grader business ever since.

ROBERT G. LeTOURNEAU...

A self-taught mechanic, Robert G. LeTourneau was a legendary innovator and manufacturer of heavy equipment. He designed some of the most important (and unusual) equipment of the twentieth century, and was a noted philanthropist.

ABOVE, INSET: *LeTourneau thrived on designing new, big, and unusual machines for specialized purposes. This LeTourneau logging transporter (photographed in the Philippines in 1957) with its oversized tires was one of his many innovations. He designed it for travel over rough skid trails, with its electric motors geared directly to each wheel.*

ABOVE: *A fleet of Model C Tournapulls and LS Carryalls, all designed and built by LeTourneau, Inc., takes a break from building the Carey Dam in Twin Falls, Idaho. The project, which involved moving more than 300,000 cubic yards of dense clay, was one of several major projects that LeTourneau helped undertake in the western United States.*

LEFT: *A LeTourneau dozer at work during World War II. LeTourneau, Inc., built thousands of machines for the Allied war effort, including 15,000 bulldozers and Angledozer blades.*

RIGHT: *Model AG Tournapull and Carryall Scraper pictured at the Tournapull Factory in Georgia in March 1942. LeTourneau was the leading designer and builder of scrapers for many years.*

AND HIS MACHINES

Like his stable of distinctive machinery, Robert Gilmour LeTourneau was one of the most compelling people to grace the world of heavy equipment. A self-taught mechanical innovator of almost mythical proportions, LeTourneau held more than 400 patents, started his own billion-dollar company, founded a university, lived an exemplary life as a Christian benefactor, and built some of the most unusual and important heavy equipment of the twentieth century.

LeTourneau was born in Vermont in 1888. He dropped out of school at the age of 14 and bounced around the country holding a series of manual labor jobs before settling in Stockton, California, in 1909 where he married, became a mechanic, and eventually, part-owner of a garage. By 1920 his business had failed. To pay off his debts LeTourneau took on work repairing a Holt crawler tractor and scraper. He soon bought his own crawler tractor and scraper and entered the scraping business. Convinced he could build a more efficient machine that would not require a second operator, he built his own scraper out of scrap metal and used motors.

During the 1920s LeTourneau's contracting work in California took off. R. G. LeTourneau, Inc., had landed several major earthmoving jobs, including the Boulder Highway to the huge Boulder Dam (later renamed Hoover Dam) in Nevada, but in 1933 LeTourneau turned his back on contracting and devoted himself exclusively to manufacturing heavy equipment. He built a plant in Peoria, Illinois, in 1935, the first of six LeTourneau plants to be constructed in the United States and Australia over the next decade. For the next 35 years LeTourneau was

the undisputed leader in innovative ways to design, build, and use scrapers.

An estimated 70 percent of the Allies' earthmoving equipment in World War II was built by LeTourneau factories. The equipment, which played a vital role in the war effort, included more than 2,000 Tournapulls, which were two-wheeled tractors used for scraping; 15,000 bulldozer and angledozer blades; 2,000 cranes; 10,000 scraper buckets; 35,000 power control units; and thousands of other machines. Among the more innovative machines was the Crash Crane used on board aircraft carriers to do everything from clearing crashed airplanes to lifting heavy ammunition, and the B30 Bomber Crane that the U.S. Air Force used to lift airplanes.

After World War II, LeTourneau continued to build earthmoving machines for the military such as a 67-ton crash pusher to shove downed airplanes off airfields, a 101-ton landing craft retriever, and massive 97-ton Tactical Crushers that cleared 32-foot-wide security strips through dense terrain during the Vietnam War.

The company continued to grow in the post-World War II years and expanded its offerings. Some of the innovations included the development of wide-based tires, electric wheels, innovative steelmaking techniques, electrical control units, braking systems, and offshore oil rigs. LeTourneau's inventions were often for unusual purposes. In the 1950s, he developed a series of "jungle crushers" to expedite the clearing of trees and underbrush in major construction projects initiated by LeTourneau in Liberia and Peru. Up to 150 tons in size, the machines consisted of 19-foot-high pushbeams that knocked over trees and then crushed them with massive rollers and

ABOVE: *Tractor equipment workshop with instructors discussing the LS Carryall Scraper and the WCK7 Angledozer.*

shearing blades. Also in the 1950s, LeTourneau invented several vehicles for traveling across snow north of the Arctic Circle. The TC-264 Sno-Buggy had eight 10-foot-diameter, wide-base tires that were inflated to just 4 pounds of pressure per square inch (psi) to traverse snow drifts. Similarly designed *sno trains* carried freight across the frozen Arctic. Elevated high above the frozen surface on giant wheels, the *trains* consisted of several cargo cars capable of traversing inhospitable terrain.

LeTourneau had established the LeTourneau Technical Institute in Longview, Texas in 1946 to provide technical training, college courses, and training for missionary technicians. The institute, one of the engineer's many philanthropic ventures, eventually became LeTourneau University, which today is an independent nondenominational comprehensive coed institution. Robert G. LeTourneau retired in 1966 and died three years later.

▲ Robert G. LeTourneau had more than 400 patents that improved scrapers, bulldozers, electric wheels, forestry equipment, excavators, cranes, assembly production, steelmaking techniques, and many other facets of heavy equipment.

Paving provides an artificial ground cover, usually asphalt or concrete, to give an all-weather surface for roadways, protect the ground from water, offer an impermeable lining to hold fluids, and/or support loads. A wide variety of paving machines perform different jobs, whether it is paving the world's largest canal, crafting a roadside curb or laying the runway at O'Hare International Airport in Chicago. The smallest machines can be operated by hand, whereas the largest trimmers can be 150 feet long. Paving machines perform two basic tasks to complete their job: They dump an aggregate material onto a prepared subsurface, and they shape the distributed material, usually as a flat surface.

Asphalt pavers consist of a tractor that powers the machine and a screed that distributes that asphalt. Prepared asphalt, already mixed and heated, is loaded onto pavers. (Asphalt is made from crushed stone, sand, gravel, slag, and mineral filler mixed together with tar and other materials that bind it together. The amount of binder in the mix is usually 3 to 12 percent.) The machine holds the asphalt in its hopper box from which a flat conveyor draws the material to the screed unit. Typically, trucks filled with asphalt will replenish the hopper box with asphalt as the machine distributes its load. The screed lays the asphalt

Paving Machines

Recent technological developments in automation have broadened the capacity of concrete pavers to do everything from narrow, tight-turning curbs and gutters to giant 150-foot-wide slabs of concrete.

The world's largest paver and trimmer as of 1996 was built by Gomaco in 1988 to pave underwater the Coachella Canal in southern California. The machine was 103 feet wide at the top, 48 feet at the bottom, and was configured to accomodate the canal's steep slopes.

TOP: *The basic equipment in laying asphalt is shown as a dump truck unloads asphalt onto a paver, which distributes it on the roadway. A paver follows the asphalt to compact the material*

ABOVE: *Giant paving machines such as this one by GOMACO are used for highways and for airport runways. They can lay slabs of concrete as wide as 50 feet.*

onto the ground and then flattens it into a permanent mat. A vibrating mechanism dissipates bubbles. Automatic controls regulate the depth and the heat of the mix.

Concrete pavers are similar in concept, but differ in detail. For one thing, concrete does not need to be heated. Dump trucks unload wet concrete into a concrete spreader that distributes the material with an auger across the width of the pavement. Recently, concrete pavers have added dowel bar inserters that inject steel rods to reinforce the pavement, avoiding the labor-intensive problem of laying the steel bars prior to spreading the cement. Following the spreader is the screed or finisher that flattens the concrete and removes excess material. Some machines have more than one screed, and some screeds have vibrating mechanisms to consolidate the concrete.

Slipform pavers have given concrete pavers a newfound flexibility. Rather than having to rely on hand-placed side forms to contain and shape the edges, slipform pavers cast the dimensions of the pavement as the machine moves forward. Moving at a pace of about 20 feet a minute, they not only set the edges of a slab of concrete, they can also lay the concrete into almost any configuration, whether it is is a curbside, a gutter, or a highway divider.

The need for giant pavers has gone through something of a recent renaissance. Large pavers were favored when the United States interstate highway system was built in the 1950s and 1960s. With the rebuilding of major highways 30 and 40 years later, the need has resurfaced. In addition, giant pavers are used for bridges, airport runways, and canals. The largest slipform pavers, such as the CMI SF-7004 and the Gomaco GP-4000, can lay 18 inches of concrete to a width of 50 feet. Each of these giant slipform pavers weighs more than 100,000 pounds; they are powered by engines with up to 460 horsepower and are 12 to 15 feet high.

The biggest machines used in the laying of concrete are finishers, which often are used for bridges and canals. These paving finishers can be as wide as 150 feet. Similar in appearance to a low steel-framed bridge, finishers are perched above the area to be paved by wheeled structures on either side. Having had the concrete poured directly, the finishing is accomplished with a long cylinder attached underneath the finisher. Because almost every canal has a different configuration and there are an almost infinite number of possibilities for bridges, finishing machines used for those purposes are put together with pin-connected sections. In the case of canals, some of the machines are designed specifically for the project. Canal pavers can pave either the floor and both sides simultaneously or one side at a time.

ABOVE: *A worker tends to an asphalt paving machine. Paving machines usually need at least one person walking along side them to both make sure the asphalt is being distributed properly and tend to stray problems.*

BELOW: *A Commander III with sideshifting trimmer by GOMACO Corporation lays a concrete curb for a 35-foot cul-de-sac in Wichita, Kansas. The development of trimmers and slip forms have greatly improved the efficiency in which concrete is laid, particularly for sharply curved curbs.*

The construction of a national highway system in the United States in the 1950s and 1960s spurred the development of large concrete pavers such as this one. Dump trucks poured the concrete as the paver distributed it to form giant slabs.

Excavators

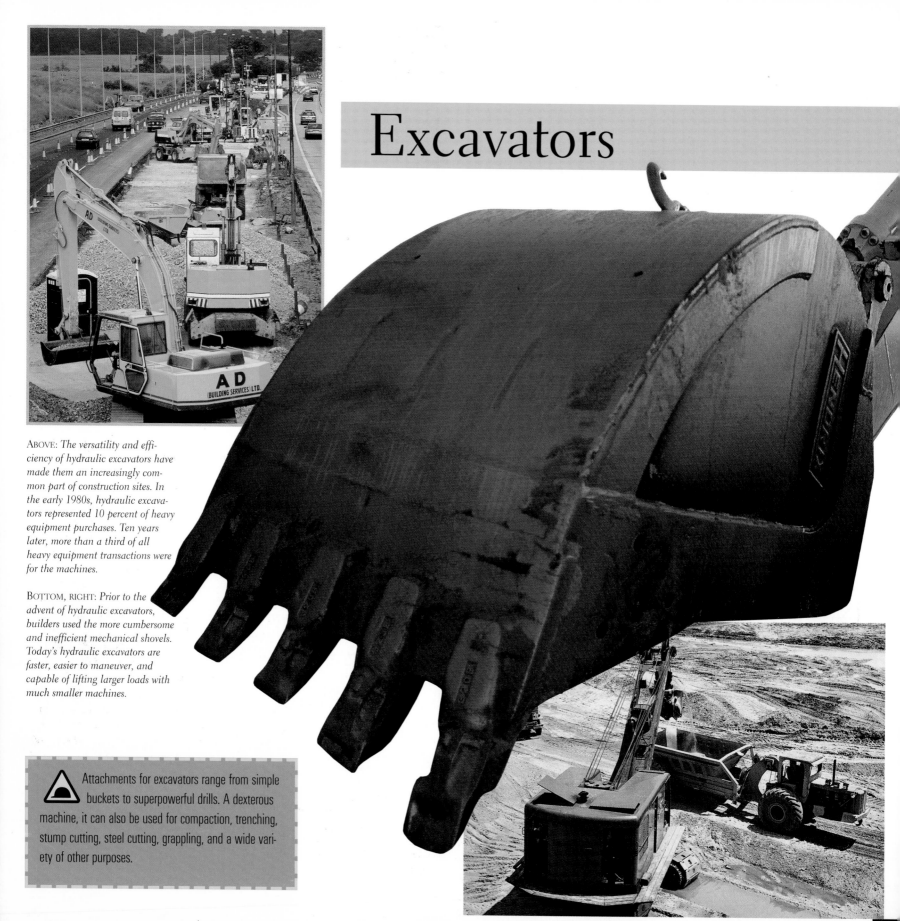

ABOVE: *The versatility and efficiency of hydraulic excavators have made them an increasingly common part of construction sites. In the early 1980s, hydraulic excavators represented 10 percent of heavy equipment purchases. Ten years later, more than a third of all heavy equipment transactions were for the machines.*

BOTTOM, RIGHT: *Prior to the advent of hydraulic excavators, builders used the more cumbersome and inefficient mechanical shovels. Today's hydraulic excavators are faster, easier to maneuver, and capable of lifting larger loads with much smaller machines.*

Attachments for excavators range from simple buckets to superpowerful drills. A dexterous machine, it can also be used for compaction, trenching, stump cutting, steel cutting, grappling, and a wide variety of other purposes.

Hydraulic excavators have rapidly evolved into an immensely useful—and thus popular—category of heavy equipment. In the early 1980s, excavators represented less than one-tenth of all construction equipment purchases. By 1996, one out of every three construction equipment transactions was for an excavator. By the year 2000, more than half of all construction machines are expected to be excavators.

Versatile, efficient, powerful, and relatively inexpensive, a modestly sized excavator can tear down a building, dig a trench, load a truck, unearth an underground tank, jackhammer a concrete wall into dust, and accomplish any number of other tasks.

Excavators are much cheaper to operate than similar-sized bulldozers or front-end loaders. The initial cost of an excavator varies according to the size and quality of the machine, but generally speaking one can expect an average 50,000-pound excavator to cost about $175,000, a 150,000-pound machine about $600,000, and a giant machine (anything more than 200,000 pounds) upwards of several million dollars.

A 100-ton excavator requires an engine with about 450 horsepower, while a bulldozer of the same weight uses an engine with 800-plus horsepower. The engine's main job in an excavator is to power its mechanized arm, not move. Most of the work that an excavator does requires the machine to stand still. In fact, most excavators will not travel faster than 3 miles an hour, a slower pace than most people walk.

The source of success for excavators, which are a comparatively modern invention, has been hydraulics, developed in the 1960s, combined with the recent advent of computer controls. The engine drives a pump that pushes hydraulic oil, which in turn powers a piston that drives the excavator's arm. Computer controls and the ingenuity of engineers have allowed for the development of powerful uses for the excavator's arm. Excavator accessories include claws, grapples, jackhammers, concrete crushers, clippers, and a wide array of buckets.

The advent of hydraulics allowed machines to move away from the more cumbersome and slow mechanical shovels. Instead of relying on cables and levers, machines use hydraulics to provide a more powerful and flexible mechanism to fulfill a multitude of tasks, so that a skilled operator can easily manipulate the 40-foot-plus boom like an enormously powerful extension of his or her arm.

Generally speaking, smaller excavators (100,000 pounds and less) serve primarily as utility machines, fulfilling a variety of different tasks with great capability. But the larger excavators (more than 100,000 pounds) tend to be used more just for loading and digging, a role that the giant excavators (more than 200,000 pounds) perform almost exclusively.

More than 150,000 excavators were produced in 1996, with almost half of them being built in Japan. About 70,000 were less than 6 tons, 75,000 were between 6 and 25 tons, and 18,000 between 25 and 75 tons. There were fewer than four hundred 75-ton-plus excavators built in 1996.

ABOVE: *The bucket is the working end of a hydraulic excavator and is the most commonly found attachment on the machine. There is an extraordinary range of other attachments that are found at the end of a hydraulic excavator's boom, including claws, grapples, jackhammers, clippers, small trenchers, tree stumpers, and other powerful implements.*

BELOW: *Most hydraulic excavators are mounted on crawlers to provide stability and power, as mobility is usually not as important for the machines. Crawler excavators typically have a top speed of 3 miles per hour. Wheeled excavators are more mobile and can travel on roads.*

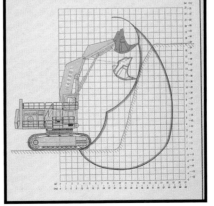

ABOVE: *This illustration of a Mannesmann Demag giant hydraulic excavator shows the machine's reach. Excavators like this are usually used for mining.*

ooking like giant chainsaws on steroids, trenchers carve ditches into the ground with frightening efficiency. The big ones make the earth shake. Smaller ones can be operated by hand. But no matter what the size, trenchers eliminate the agony of backaches that used to be associated with digging ditches.

The advantage of a trencher is that it removes as little material as possible when laying cables or pipes. It allows you to dig a ditch the width of whatever it is you are laying into the ground.

The largest trenchers are monstrous.

Vermeer Manufacturing, which has one of the widest ranges of trenchers, makes the T-1455, a 60-foot-long machine, almost half the length of which consists of a tremendous boom. As wide as 4 ½ feet, the boom can go as deep as 20 feet into the ground. The T-1455 weighs 90 tons, is driven by a 675-horsepower engine, and costs about $750,000 to buy new. Carbide-tipped cutters on a metal-plate conveyor dig into the earth, cutting solid rock, frost and frozen earth, and whatever else gets in the way.

On the other end of the spectrum are walk-behind trenchers whose blades are a modest 2 to 3 feet long. Petite by giant

Trenchers

▲ The largest trenchers have blades that are 4 to 5 feet wide and will dig trenches 20 feet deep.

ABOVE: *The boom of a giant trencher cut a narrow ditch 20 feet deep into the earth. Its engine is fixed with 675-horsepower.*

trencher standards, they are still a handful to operate, weighing in at 850 pounds. Ditch Witch is a major manufacturer of trenchers of all sizes, and Trencore manufactures large trenchers.

There is also a wide range of trencher plows with trench attachments placed on the rear of modestly sized plows with a dozer blade and/or backhoe on the front. Having dug the trench, the machine can then push the dirt and rocks back into the ditch. Some machines even have attachments that lay the cable or pipe into the ground, thus providing three tasks with a single machine.

In situations where the rock is too hard for a trencher, a rock-cutter attachment can often be used. Stronger and narrower than trenchers, the rock wheels cut solid rock. The alternative to this is usually explosives.

Trenchers are ideal machines for digging extended trenches used for sewers, pipelines, and cables. Using a trencher with a 10-foot boom in difficult conditions, an operator takes between 45 minutes and an hour to dig a 50-foot-long trench that is 4 feet deep. Although trenchers used to be difficult to operate, a new electronic control system that automatically adjusts the track speed and tracking has simplified their operation.

BOTTOM: *A relatively primitive trencher by modern standards cuts a drainage ditch using a miniature bucket wheel excavator mechanism.*

BELOW: *Able to dig trenches 20 feet deep, the T-1455 is one of the largest trenchers built and the biggest one manufactured by Vermeer. The imposing machine weighs 90 tons, and is 60 feet long, and its massive blade bristles with carbide-tipped cutters.*

CATERPILLAR

▲ Sales outside the United States represented more than half of Caterpillar's business in 1996. The company—the largest manufacturer of heavy equipment in the world—has 61 plants, 29 of them outside the United States.

Caterpillar's trademark yellow machines are a common site on almost any construction project. Views such as this one in which almost every machine is a Caterpillar are not unusual. Caterpillar machines here include four scrapers, two dump trucks, two bulldozers, and a hydraulic excavator.

INSET, BELOW: *The Caterpillar D11 is one of the largest earthmoving machines made by Caterpillar. It weighs 215,000 pounds and is powered by a 770-horsepower engine.*

Caterpillar is the largest manufacturer of heavy equipment in the world today. With hundreds of different machinery lines ranging from simple compactors to giant computer-operated dump trucks to the engines that drive oils rigs, Caterpillar is omnipresent in the world of heavy equipment. It has annual sales of $16 billion and a worldwide workforce of 57,000 people. The rise of Caterpillar in many ways reflects the history of heavy equipment in modern times.

The origins of Caterpillar date back to the late nineteenth century with two companies: the Stockton Wheel Company in California with Benjamin Holt as president, and Daniel Best's Best Manufacturing in Oakland, California. Like most equipment manufacturers in the 1800s, the companies built farm machinery. Best specialized in grain cleaners, and the Stockton Wheel Company made carriages and wheels.

With the advent of steam engines and the invention of combine harvesters, both companies developed their own versions of the revolutionary steam-driven machinery. In 1904, Holt developed a track-type tractor, which he dubbed a "Caterpillar." His company soon used gasoline engines to replace the steam engines, and rapid sales ensued. Best sold his company to Holt in 1908, although his son, C. L. Best, formed a new tractor manufacturing company soon afterward, which later merged with Caterpillar in 1925.

Holt opened a manufacturing plant in Peoria, Illinois, in 1910, the start of an almost century-old relationship between the city and Caterpillar, which has seen as much as 25 percent of the region's workforce employed by Caterpillar.

Early in the development of automobiles, Holt realized the potential that road construction offered his company. He became a forceful advocate of new roads and developed machinery to level, grade, and build roads. The outbreak of World War I also opened opportunities for the company. The track-type tractor served as a model for the development of the tank on the Western Front in Europe, but more significantly the reliability and sturdiness of the Caterpillar tractors led to soaring sales and interest in the machines. Caterpillar became world famous. The company built upon that reputation in the 1920s, and sales soared to more than $50 million in 1929. The workforce totaled 4,000 people.

The Great Depression of the 1930s burst the expansion, and sales collapsed (although orders totaling $12 million in 1929 and 1930 for collective farms in the Soviet Union helped stem the losses). Total sales in 1932, nevertheless, were a mere $13.3 million. Fortunately for the company, its researchers had developed a new diesel engine that cut operating costs for tractors. The Diesel 60 tractor proved to be very popular and helped pull Caterpillar out of its slump. In another development, the company switched its color scheme in 1932 from red and gray to a new "Hi-Way Yellow," which has become familiar to most construction sites across the world.

World War II propelled the company into extraordinary growth. Demand soared for its bulldozers, tractors, and other equipment. The bulldozer, in particular, became a critical tool in the military's arsenal of equipment to wage war. Unlike World War I, when sales dipped after the armistice, Caterpillar's business continued to surge with the end of the war. The economy in the United States boomed, and Europe needed to be rebuilt. Caterpillar grew by leaps and bounds, building new factories and acquiring other companies.

As the demands grew and changed, Caterpillar adjusted or expanded its products. Scrapers, graders, and bulldozers were built to accommodate the highway construction boom of the 1950s and 1960s in the United States. New plants were established overseas in Europe and later Asia and Australia to meet foreign demand. The company developed and built mining equipment, pipelayers, smaller machinery for home construction, and engines to serve an ever-expanding demand for increasingly sophisticated and specialized equipment. By 1967, Caterpillar had produced 27 percent of the Free World's construction equipment. And in 1981, sales totaled $9.2 billion, a 700-fold increase in sales since 1932.

A deep recession, a devalued dollar, labor strife, and increased competition all took their toll on Caterpillar in the 1980s, but the company continues to be an international leader in terms of quality, technological innovation, and sheer size.

TIRES, TRACKS, AND OTHER MODES OF MOVING MACHINES

Ignoring the well-known advice that there is no need to reinvent the wheel, heavy equipment designers have, in fact, invented and improved different kinds of wheels and other ways to move large machinery. Wheels do essentially three things for equipment: distribute the machine's weight along the ground, provide traction for its operation, and steer the machine. Innovations in how to best accomplish these goals have resulted in an extraordinary range of wheels, tracks, tires, and hydraulic mechanisms to move giant machines. What was once simply a question of whether to use a solid wooden wheel or a spoked wooden wheel has become much more complicated.

Tires

Tires were first applied to heavy equipment in the 1930s on tractors and road construction equipment. There are two basic types of tires. Radial tires are reinforced with steel to strengthen the rubber and bias tires, which are bolstered with nylon cords. Radial tires are stronger, more durable, and more expensive. In general, tires allow the equipment to go faster, be more mobile, and travel on public roads. They typically do not have as much traction as tracks and the ground pressure tends to be higher because there is not as much area touching the ground as tracks. Giant wheeled-tractors often lessen the soil compaction by placing four or even six wheels per axle. Tires are also limited by their capacity to withstand the heat that is generated from the weight and traveling speed of the machines.

A tire's strength is given a ton-miles-per-hour rating that is based on its ability to carry a determined amount of weight up to a certain speed. The faster the wheel moves and the more weight it is carrying, the greater the heat applied. When the temperature gets too high, the tire bursts. In recent years, one of the main obstacles for building bigger giant trucks has been the technology and the costs involved in making tires strong enough to carry loads of 300-plus tons. It is not simply a question of making the tires bigger, but rather developing stronger materials and having enough demand to justify the exorbitant expense of crafting new molds for a very limited market. As it is, the list price for a single tire on a 300-ton truck is $70,000.

Crawler tracks provide stability, strength, and in cases like this grading capacity. The way a crawler moves is that a sprocket drive at the rear of the mechanism meshes with the track that extends over and around other idle sprockets.

In 1978, Caterpillar began producing bulldozers with the elevated sprocket design. By placing the sprocket drive in an elevated position, the company claims that it improves the strength, reliability, and operating costs of the mechanism. Almost all of Caterpillar's dozers today operate with an elevated sprocket.

Crawler Tracks

Crawler tracks were first applied to heavy equipment in 1901 when Alvin C. Lombard of Maine invented his Lombard Steam Log Hauler to free horses from having to pull sleds over iced roads in the northern United States and Canada. A few years later and on the other side of the United States, Benjamin Holt (one of the two founders of Caterpillar Inc.) developed a similar rotating crawler band for steam tractors in California. The way a crawler works is that a large sprocket similar to a gear is placed at the rear of the mechanism. The gear meshes with the track that extends across several other sprockets, goes under the gears, and is reconnected in the rear. As the sprocket turns, it forces the machine to propel forward. Seeing the crawler in action, an observer told Holt that the tractor moved like a "caterpillar." Holt quickly adapted the description as the name of the crawler track and ultimately his company.

At the time, heavy equipment used either tracks, which greatly limited their mobility, or wheels. The sheer weight of the steam-powered machines, however, was frequently too great for the wheels, which sunk into the ground. Crawler tracks provided both mobility and stability. Modern crawler tracks continue to offer the same advantages, though they are slower than wheels, tend to be more expensive, and usually cannot be operated on roads. Several companies, however, have recently added rubber to the tracks (which are made of steel), which allows the machinery to go on roads. The most common application for rubber tracks is for Caterpillar's Challenger tractors. By using rubber tracks instead of tires, the company claims to reduce soil compaction without sacrificing speed and mobility.

The costs and technology involved in manufacturing giant tires have been among the most significant limiting factors in the construction of even bigger giant dump trucks.

Up until the early part of the twentieth century few people even attempted to reinvent the wheel. Instead, manufacturers just used different materials such as metal for the tried-and-true hub-and-spoke wheel dating back to ancient times. One of the many shortcomings of a bare wheel is that any significant amount of weight sinks the wheel into the ground.

Oversized tires are frequently used for vehicles to go over sand, snow, and other soft terrain. In the 1950s, Robert LeTourneau designed several vehicles with giant tires with very low air pressure for that purpose.

Walking Mechanisms

In 1913, Oscar Martinson invented a walking pontoon device that was capable of moving the largest machines over soft terrain by dispersing the weight over an even larger area. The system, which is still used today by giant walking draglines, included extended "feet" on either side of the machine's superstructure. Each pontoon was divided into a pair of sections. The mechanism moved the machine in a method similar to that of a person's walking. One part of each section was raised and then stepped forward (or backward) while the other sections sustained the burden of the machine. Once the first sections moved, the rear section would perform a similar motion, thus moving the entire machine forward (or backward). The concept for today's giant walking draglines is remarkably similar, with the major changes being the advances in technology and hydraulics to greatly increase the strength and lifting capacity of the walking pontoons.

The undercarriage of a massive stripping shovel consists of the car body, crawler frames and crawler shoe belts, propel machinery, and other components. The crawlers in this illustration for a P & H 5700 stripping shovel are 45 feet long and more than 8 feet wide.

Electric Wheels

Electric wheels were developed in the early 1960s to provide power directly to giant tire wheels as much as 122 inches in diameter. Each wheel has its own electric engine fed by the central diesel-electric generating system. This eliminates the heavy weight and friction of conventional power train components (the transmission, differential, and wheel shaft). With the exception of Caterpillar's giant trucks, most giant dump trucks larger than 120 tons use electric wheels.

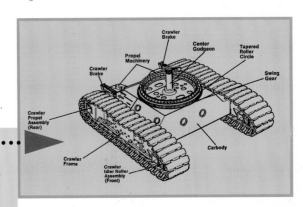

A TOUCH, AN EYE, AND RESPECT:

What It Takes to Be a Heavy Equipment Operator

David J. Bowler gets behind the controls of the Caterpillar D6 bulldozer and prepares to move a small mountain of topsoil that had been set aside for the lawns of a new subdivision in Pittsfield, Massachusetts. The machine, with its massive high-sprocket tracks, is made for the big push. It will make easy work of the mountain.

Though only 31 years old, Bowler has had his operator's license for 12 years. He started as a laborer with the David J. Tierney Construction Company in Pittsfield when he was straight out of high school.

"At the time, I was running a rake and a shovel," Bowler recalled, "and I was fascinated by the heavy equipment."

Tierney's two operators, Harold Hinkley and Eddie Bushey, were experienced men who were 58 and 59 years old, respectively. Bowler knew their days with the company were numbered, and he wasn't thrilled with the idea of using his back for the rest of his life. He started training to obtain his operator's license.

"Harold and Eddie worked with me," Bowler said. "They showed me an awful lot. But most of this you learn by the seat of your pants. The more you do it, the more comfortable you become with the machines."

He tapped the side of the bulldozer. "Running this is like second nature to me," he said.

To Bowler, that is the most important rule of operation. Gaining complete familiarity with the machines and their potential is the difference between a safe and efficient job and possible disaster.

"If you aren't comfortable with the machine, you're going to hurt yourself or some-

ABOVE: *Heavy equipment on the move makes for exciting construction sites. Here a scraper and a bulldozer stir up some dust in the rising sun.*

LEFT: *Blending power and a delicate touch, a construction worker helps position a crane to lift a 13 foot-diameter concrete water pipe in California.*

one else," he said. "I know how far I can tip. That's a must. When I first started running a bulldozer, I'd get up on a rock and hold on for dear life. Now I know the pitch."

In time, Bowler had the confidence to stretch his own skills, as well as the power of the equipment. But he is still respectful of tons of metal on a construction site swarming with people, particularly when it comes to cranes.

"One thing Eddie told me is that the day I think I know everything about running a crane is the day I'm going to get into trouble," Bowler continued. "Every job is different. You've got to know your load and you've got to know the machine's limit."

He recalled the day he was lifting 2,000-pound air-conditioning units to the roof of a three-story building. Eager to get to work, the plumber on the job was rushing him. But Bowler is cautious by nature and believes in the merits of a dry run before dangling the massive units over the heads of the guys on the roof.

"I told him when I'm running a crane, I've got two speeds: slow and slower," Bowler said. "If he didn't like this speed, he definitely wasn't going to like the other."

And so Bowler painstakingly set up the lift,

LEFT: *At the gears of a paving machine, an operator scans his construction site.*

BELOW: *A backhoe operator braces for what looks like what may be a long day's work by the lake.*

positioning the machine and putting the ball of the crane right in the center of where the roof unit had to go.

"By then, I knew I was in the right spot and the machine would lift that far," he said. "People try to tell me what I can do all the time. Never let anybody else tell you how to run your machine. I've never been in a situation I didn't want to be in."

Bowler observed that a lot of people have been killed in crane accidents, and he does not want to add to the statistics. His boss sent him to a school for crane operation in South Carolina that was taught by a crane accident investigator. On the first day, the teacher spent three hours showing a documentary he had made of crane accidents.

"There were ten guys in the class," Bowler said. "When we went out on break, not one of

us ever wanted to run a crane again. We all realized its power."

One of the golden rules of operating heavy equipment is the absolute need to "have eyes everywhere," Bowler said.

Digging holes, moving mountains of earth, or booming construction equipment up to a multistory building site takes on a certain lulling cadence. In regular patterns, the operator does a soft-shoe dance on the foot pedals that move the giant tracks, adjust the level of the cab, and control the bucket. With the same regularity, the operator manipulates the hand controls. The rhythm can be mesmerizing.

"But there are people all around you," he said. "You have to be completely aware of your environment."

The young operator said that over the course of years working with the same people,

a sense of trust builds on both sides. On most days there are hordes of laborers working within feet of his massive steel bucket. All around him vehicles are pulling in and out of the site. His 1280 Case excavator, which is a workhorse on most jobs, can also be a lethal weapon.

"They know my every move, and I know what they're going to do next," he said of the construction crew. "You have to build that respect and confidence."

The operator's eyes necessarily extend to other details as well.

"You have to be able to see a grade," Bowler said, referring to high and low elevations on a site that can be almost imperceptible to the untrained eye. Easing away the high spots, building up the low, and blending the two so that water will never pool in unwanted areas—these make the difference between a road or a yard that will stand up over time or one that will wash out with the first heavy rain.

"Everybody has an idea about how a place should look," Bowler said. "The heavy equipment operator's job is to take those ideas and make them work."

ABOVE: *A John Deere front-end loader does its work despite the debris, dust, and sun.*

RIGHT: *Combining a bridge paver, large crane, and manpower, this construction team prepares to pave a bridge.*

CRANES

Cranes dot the horizon of the Charles-de-Gaulle
Airport outside of Paris as a major construction
project is under way.

There is very little that is quite as spectacular as a giant crane on a city block lifting a load of materials to the top of a skyscraper with a single cable. Looming high in the sky, cranes make light work of heavy tasks and at the same time are a pretty picture. The setting sun behind a large crane is almost a visual cliché. It is not just the size of cranes that is amazing, but also the physics involved. You can look at a giant shovel or truck and say, "Whoa, is that big!" With a giant crane there is another exclamation point and a question mark: "How does it do that!!?"

Using pulleys, levers, and ropes, ancient builders devised ways to move large objects short distances. While they may not have had engines, modern technology, and reinforced metals to do their work, they did have physics. Men like the Greek mathematician Archimedes figured out ways to use simple tools to accomplish heavy tasks. Today's cranes use many of the same principles, but they are bigger and stronger, and they are mobile. The irony is that by using the laws of physics cranes seem to defy the laws of gravity.

PRIMER ON CRANES

Cranes represent one of the oldest forms of machinery. Their purpose is to lift heavy loads, swing them horizontally, and then secure the load for release. There are many different types of cranes, ranging from simple stationary lifting mechanisms to gigantic, impossibly complicated behemoths as tall as skyscrapers. They can be mobile or in a fixed position.

A crawler crane with a lattice boom helps prepare the foundation for the construction of a high-rise apartment building.

A shipbuilding gantry crane, or bridge crane, offers powerful hoisting capacity, but it is limited in its reach and ability to move objects beyond the confines of the overhead bridge.

Ancient Cranes, Timeless Principles

Although Isaac Newton wasn't around at the time to explain the physics or quantify the forces involved, ancient societies applied basic engineering principles to develop the first primitive cranes. The earliest cranes combined the concepts of a pulley and a lever to hoist objects that were too big for human strength alone to move. A fixed vertical wooden beam was secured to the ground from which a hoisting rope was attached either at the top of the mast or at the end of another beam that was attached. Using either a single pulley or several, workers could leverage their muscle power to lift materials and place them in the desired location. Some cranes had more than one mast to strengthen the lifting capacity of the crane. Primitive cranes were used for a wide variety of construction purposes in ancient times including the construction of the Egyptian pyramids and the marvels of ancient Roman buildings, roads, coliseums, and aqueducts. The advent of motorized engines, vastly improved metal-making capabilities, and modern technology have, of course, dramatically improved the capacities of cranes, but the fundamental principles of using levers and pulleys to leverage a crane's ability to lift heavy objects have not changed.

A grab is often used for cranes to pick up bulk materials such as coal or ore. It consists of two shells, operated by a holding rope and closing rope, which can open and close to grab the load and discharge it.

Crane Safety

As spectacular as cranes are to behold when they are doing their jobs right, they can also cause spectacular damage when things go wrong. By their very nature, cranes are big, tall, and heavy, and whenever they lift heavy objects, they place a strain on both the machine's structural strength and on its ability to remain upright. If something breaks or tips, the whole thing comes crashing down, sometimes with fatal results. Indeed, most heavy equipment operators say that cranes are the most dangerous of the huge machines they operate.

Two categories of things can go wrong with a crane. One is structural damage: something breaks, erodes, or snaps within the crane itself. The other type of problem occurs when the load is so big that it causes the crane to overturn. To help prevent both kinds of accidents, international standards outlining the capacity of cranes have been established based on complex calculations measuring all the known forces that will be applied to a crane and also based on experiments with the equipment and the measurement of the strain different loads place on it. When the lifting capacity of a crane is determined, a stability margin is also placed on it. If the stability margin is rated at 85 percent, that means the listed capacity is 85 percent of the calculated load that will cause the crane to overturn. Experts design cranes to prevent these sorts of problems; the creation of low centers of gravity, and the use of strong but lightweight steel structures and heavy counterweights at the base of the crane are among a host of other preventive measures.

Powerful gantry cranes line the harbor at Saint Nazaire, France.

The 650-ton Demag AC 1600 Telescopic Crane has a 594-horsepower engine for its truck, a 303-horsepower engine to power the crane's superstructure, and a 108-ton counterweight. It is 68 feet long and has a lifting capacity of 650 tons. Its main telescopic boom reaches 164 feet into the air, but with additional jibs it can lift items as high as 443 feet off the ground.

Mobile versus Tower Cranes

As a general rule, Europeans tend to favor using freestanding tower cranes, but in the United States the bias is toward mobile cranes and roof-mounted derricks. Why is this? A quick look at the advantages and disadvantages of each type of crane and the typical situation in each part of the world answers the question. Builders must carefully consider a variety of issues when they decide which type of crane to use.

Freestanding tower cranes require less surface area on the ground to build, can have the benefit of a reinforced base built into the ground (and thus greater lifting capacity), tend to have greater reach with their booms, can reach higher into the sky, have faster lifting speeds, and are able to withstand higher wind speeds. Mobile cranes, on the other hand, are much easier to move from site to site, have similar maximum lifting capacities, and are less expensive. Their relatively limited reach is offset when complemented with fixed cranes placed on top of a building.

Thus, when an engineer decides what type of crane to use, he or she considers issues such as the weight of the material to be lifted, the amount of surface area available for the crane, the heights to which materials must be lifted, the cost, the crane's radius, and the amount of time the crane will be in place. In Europe, cities tend to be more congested with little surface space for mobile cranes to maneuver—thus tower cranes have been the preferred option. In the United States, heavy structural steel has been used for tall buildings. Initially, tower cranes did not have the high pull lines to lift them adequately, so builders leaned toward using a combination of mobile cranes and fixed cranes placed on top of the buildings.

Bridge and Jib Cranes

A bridge crane usually consists of two upright girders that support a "bridge" from which a winch lifts loads. The winch can be positioned anywhere along the bridge and is often mobile, able to swing from one end of the bridge to the other. The girders usually travel along a track that is either on the ground or suspended from a ceiling. Bridge cranes, which are typically used for industrial purposes, can lift very heavy loads but are restricted in their mobility by their tracks.

A jib crane has an arm known as a *jib* or boom that is attached near or at the top of the crane's tower on a vertical pivot. The boom (or jib) moves material horizontally by swinging on the pivot in what is called a *slewing* motion. The jib can also perform a *luffing* or *derricking* motion in which it raises or lowers its load by changing its inclination angle with the tower. Through these two types of motion, slewing and luffing, the jib can position its load to any point within a certain radius. The radius is defined by the length of the jib and the crane's lifting capacity. The tighter the radius, the greater the crane's lifting capability.

A counterweight is applied to a crane to prevent heavy loads from tipping a crane forward. The counterweight, however, has to be designed so that it is not so heavy as to tip the machine backward. To provide maximum stability, cranes are designed to disperse weight as widely and evenly as possible. This is why the largest mobile cranes have up to 18 wheels.

This construction crane in Athens, Greece, is a typical example of a hammerhead tower crane frequently used for erecting buildings. A tower crane's lifting capacity at great radii does not drop off nearly as rapidly as a mobile crane's.

Mounted on sometimes extraordinary trucks, wheeled cranes offer the strength of powerful hoisting machines and the flexibility of easy mobility. The largest of these cranes have carriages that are larger than tractor-trailer trucks, booms that can reach the tops of skyscrapers hundreds of feet high, and the capacity to lift hundreds of tons of material. As impressive as they are to look at, they are also very dangerous machines, capable of tipping and causing spectacular accidents. Moreso than with other wheeled equipment, safety, as much as capacity, is a driving factor influencing the design of giant wheeled cranes because so many different things can go wrong—with fatal results.

Ranging in lift capacity from less than 5 tons to 1,000 tons, wheeled cranes have the advantage of being able to move from job to job with little hassle and, up to certain capacities, do not require another rigging crane for assistance. Mobile cranes typically have a maximum capacity similar to that of tower cranes, but they cannot reach as far out with heavy objects. They also tend to have lower maximum heights, take up more space at the foundation, and are more costly to maintain. As opposed to crawler cranes, wheeled cranes are simpler to set up, tend not to be as powerful, and cannot travel with their hoisted loads.

Mobile cranes are designed to maximize the machine's capacity by using strong and stiff structural steel, low weight mass, and light (but strong) materials for the boom. All mobile cranes are equipped with hefty outriggers that can quickly be set with jack legs to provide a wide, stable base for the vehicle. The stability of the crane is also determined by ground conditions. The softer and less level the ground, the less stable the crane. Boom extensions and fly jibs greatly expand mobile cranes' basic boom system with added capacity, both in terms of how high the cranes can reach and how far they can extend their radii. The weight of a load hoisted by a mobile crane falls off much more dramatically the farther out the boom goes compared with tower cranes. Increasingly sophisticated alarm systems are used in mobile cranes to warn operators of potential dangers.

There are several different types of wheeled cranes. The two different types of booms are *lattice* and *telescopic*, or *cantilevered*. Lattice booms are made of metal struts and are not as flexible in their uses as telescopic booms. With advances in hydraulic power and metal structural capacity, telescopic booms have become more common. These booms are usually composed of three or four concentric pipe sections (typically in a rounded or trapezoidal-type structure) that telescope up and out with the biggest section at the base and other sections getting smaller as it extends outward. As the boom extends outward each section goes out a proportional amount so that the tapered shape matches the bending movement caused by the load.

Rough-Terrain Cranes

Another distinction between wheeled cranes is their ability to travel on public roads and traverse rough ground. Mobile cranes mounted on single-engine, self-propelled wheel mountings are known as *rough-terrain cranes*, which are designed for use (as the names implies) on rugged ground. All rough-terrain cranes have four-wheel drive and an outrigger system. Their maximum lifting capacity typically ranges from 30 to 100 tons. The machines are not allowed on public roads in western Europe. Grove manufactures one of the largest rough-terrain cranes, the RT9100 Rough Terrain Hydraulic Crane. Its main boom has a maximum reach of 114 feet, but the addition of an optional jib or lattice extension increases the maximum height up to 208 feet. It is powered by a 250-horsepower engine and has a maximum lifting capacity of 100 tons.

All-Terrain or Truck Cranes

All-terrain cranes are mounted on trucklike carriages with as many as nine axles, which help provide additional stability. Their lifting capacity ranges from less than 10 tons up to 1,000 tons. Several added features allow them to traverse unimproved or rough ground, maneuver in tight positions, and position themselves in a safe, secure, and stable manner for hoisting in all but the most precarious locations. Sophisticated suspension systems allow the crane operator to lift and lower wheels to conform to the contour of the ground, thus keeping the base of the crane level even if it is sitting on a hill or uneven terrain. Crab steering in which all of the tires can be steered individually allows the large vehicle to easily maneuver awkward layouts.

The Mannesmann Demag AC 1600, for example, is one of the largest mobile telescopic cranes. Its lifting capacity is 650 tons. The 68-foot-long, 13-foot-high vehicle has nine axles with eighteen tires and four large outriggers that form a square 39 feet long on each side. Its main four-section telescopic boom can

ABOVE: *Mobile cranes, such as this Grove all-terrain crane, are a common sight at electrical plant construction sites. Although they have the advantage of being highly mobile, they also require significantly more room to maneuver both into and out of position.*

ABOVE, INSET: *A four-axle truck crane loads a tractor trailer truck. Not as sophisticated or strong as contemporary mobile cranes, this crane seems to be simply placed on the back of a truck bed.*

reach 164 feet into the sky, or about the height of a 16-story building. The addition of a fly jib more than doubles its maximum lifting height to 387 feet. And the use of a luffing fly jib pushes the height capacity to 443 feet, or higher than a 40-story building. While a jib extends the reach of the crane, the farther out it reaches, the lower the crane's maximum weight capacity for the extend locations. Demag, like other crane manufacturers, offers the option of applying extra leverage and thus lifting capacity with what it calls a "Superlift" attachment near the base of the main boom.

The German heavy equipment manufacturer Liebherr makes several giant cranes, including the powerful Liebherr LTM 1800, an eight-axle vehicle with a 570-horsepower engine that can lift up to 1,000 tons. With additional jibs, its maximum height is 479 feet with a horizontal reach of up to 354 feet. The similar LG 1550 can lift 700 tons, but its boom can be extended to 541 feet (or the height of a 50-story building) with a horizontal reach of up to 407 feet (at which point the maximum load has fallen steeply to only 5,500 pounds).

Loader Cranes

Another common, but entirely different, category of mobile cranes is the *loader crane*. These cranes are truck-mounted booms that are attached to flatbed trucks to load and unload material onto and from the truck itself. They are designed exclusively for handling materials and not for erecting structures. The booms can be mounted or dismounted from the truck bed and are usually attached next to the truck's cab to distribute the load to all axles of the truck. There are scores of different types of loader cranes. Boom lengths are usually in the 30- to 40-foot range, although there are some with reaches of 100 feet or more. As with other cranes, jibs can be added to extend the boom's reach. Most loader cranes have a maximum lifting capacity of under 40 tons, although there are some that exceed 100 tons, such as the Effer 140/N and the Heila HLR140000/4S, both of which can lift more than 150 tons of material.

MOBILE WHEELED CRANES

ABOVE: *The 500-ton-capacity Liebherr LTM 1400 mobile crane is one of the larger wheeled cranes built by the German manufacturer. The eight-axle crane can lift objects as high as 433 feet with a jib attachment—that's as high as a 40-story building.*

RIGHT: *A wheeled crane can be very handy on construction sites for moving heavy materials. Operators, however, have to be very careful they do not exceed the load capacities. Modern mobile cranes have computerized warning systems to assist operators.*

RIGHT: *Crawler cranes are a common sight at ports as they move goods back and forth on docks, ships, and barges. This crane is helping to move 1,219 trucks bound for Indonesia onto barges at the Port of Baltimore in 1976.*

CRAWLER CRANES

Crawler cranes have the strongest lifting capacity of any mobile lifting machines. Similar to wheeled mobile cranes, they sacrifice mobility for lifting capacity. Recent innovations combining fixed attachments to crawler cranes have increased their lifting ability to even greater heights. Crawler cranes have the advantage of being able to work in less stable terrain than most wheeled cranes; that's because the wide and long tracks allow for the crane's weight to be spread over a larger bearing. Crawler cranes offer the additional benefit of being more easily converted for excavation purposes. Unlike wheeled mobile cranes, however, crawler cranes are not self-transporting. They usually do not travel faster than walking speed and must be moved from site to site on trucks.

The massive Liebherr LR 11200 has the world's highest reach for mobile cranes. With a maximum height of 247 yards, it can lift up to 1,476 tons. Two of these cranes are in operation in Japan to maintain filter systems on 600-foot-high chimneys in power stations and perform several other tasks. MIC Engineering Company paid $38 million to Liebherr-Werk Ehingen for the giant machines, whose operational weight is 2,362 tons. Each one uses six winches to control 4.52 miles of rope. The massive crane can lift 984 tons at a radius of 19 yards, 2 feet; 98 tons at a radius of 109 yards, and 29.5 tons at a 171-yard radius. The width of its steel pads is nearly 8 feet, and the crawlers are almost 40 feet long. The main boom is 138 yards long, the luffing jib is 122 yards long, and an extra derrick mast is 46 yards long. A 12-cylinder, 1,014-horsepower Cummins engine powers the machine, whose counterweight can be 394 tons.

Recent innovations have allowed crane engineers to further strengthen giant crawler cranes. Crane manufacturers Van Seumeren Holland and Mannesmann Demag have designed a new system in which a horizontal beam attached to the top of the boom's tip is given additional support by a vertical crane mast. This provides extra strength and stability for the crawler crane to lift heavier loads, up to 2,214 tons. The kinds of objects that require the lifting might of the Van Seumeran Crane-Mast (VSCM) include huge loads for power stations, offshore platforms, chemical and petrochemical plants, and other infrastructure projects.

Another, albeit less spectacular, way to strengthen a crawler crane is to use a ringer configuration. Generally speaking, this type of arrangement more than doubles the lifting capacity of the crawler crane by distributing and improving the amount of ground pressure. The downside is that it severely limits the crane's mobility. When Manitowoc used a 45-foot-diameter ringer attachment for its 888 series-2 cranes, the maximum rated lift capacity was increased from 230 to 600 tons. Assembly time for the machines, which have a list price of about $2.5 million, is two to three days.

LEFT: *Particularly in the United States, crawler cranes work in tandem with small tower cranes on top of buildings to lift heavy materials to the top of skyscrapers, such as this construction site in Houston, Texas.*

ABOVE: *Crawler cranes are well-suited for lifting large objects to high places. Here one positions cement at a New York City hotel that is under construction.*

BELOW: *An American A-1000 crawler crane in action in central Colorado. The rear mast section sticking out at the base of the main boom provides leverage to give the crane greater hoisting strength.*

TOWER CRANES

LEFT: *Kroll Cranes claims that its K-10000 is the world's largest hammerhead tower crane, capable of lifting more than 500,000 pounds at a radius of 144 feet. Here the K-10000 is at work at the Seabrook, New Hampshire, nuclear power plant.*

▲ The advantages of tower cranes are their stability, extended reach, and the small surface area required for the base. The main disadvantage of tower cranes versus mobile cranes is that they are expensive and cumbersome to erect.

Picture two Statues of Liberty atop one another with an arm sticking straight out that is the length of a football field. That is about the size of the Kroll 10000 tower crane, one of the largest and most powerful of all the tower cranes in the world. Capable of lifting 100 tons as high as 400 feet, the crane's reach is close to 100 yards and is often used for the construction of major infrastructure facilities such as power plants, chemical plants, and off-shore drilling platforms. The crane is so big that it includes a second smaller crane at the top that is used for the construction and maintenance of the upper portions of the main crane and its booms. By most standards, this auxiliary crane is very large in its own right with a reach of more than 100 feet.

Dismantled, the Kroll 10000 tower crane is an unimposing sight, similar to a children's giant Erector set neatly laid out on the ground. But put the large steel frames together the way they are supposed to be erected, and you have yourself a monster of a machine. This is no simple task, however. Depending on the work conditions and the amount of distance to transport the dismantled crane, it can cost between $150,000 and $1 million just to build a giant tower crane. The Kroll 10000, which

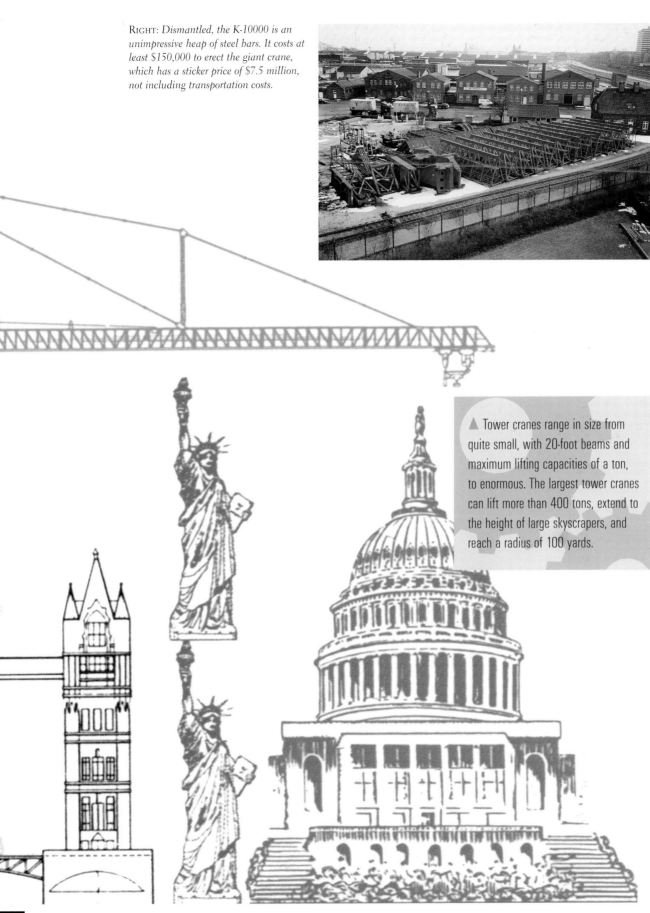

▲ Tower cranes range in size from quite small, with 20-foot beams and maximum lifting capacities of a ton, to enormous. The largest tower cranes can lift more than 400 tons, extend to the height of large skyscrapers, and reach a radius of 100 yards.

costs about $7.5 million to buy, requires more than 100 oversized trucks to transport all its pieces. It then costs $4,000 or more a truck to haul the materials a significant distance.

The great advantage of a tower crane, like all other tower cranes, is that it only requires a small amount of land to build its stable base. The Kroll 10000, for example, is built on a square base with 28 feet in each side. Further, a tower crane has tremendous reach not only to move material high above the ground but also to cover extensive ground. Typically, the alternative to using a giant tower crane for a project such as a utility plant is employing several large crawler or wheeled cranes that surround a facility under construction. The mobile cranes, however, do not have the same reach and require more space to gain access to the site. Also, a mobile crane's capacity to lift heavy materials falls off dramatically the farther out its reach. Generally speaking, the more stable tower cranes are able to hold heavier materials at greater radii. In some cases, limiting factors of a tower crane's dimensions are not the machine's superstructure components, but rather the capability of the hoists and cables. The weight if the rope is what reduces the lifting capacity of a tower crane as hook heights increase, for instance.

Tower cranes have been widely used in Europe for many years for both large buildings and modestly sized houses. Until recently they were not very popular in the United States where contractors preferred the more familiar crawler and wheeled cranes. In the 1980s, however, builders started to see the advantages of the more powerful tower cranes when lifting modular components. The tower crane allows contractors to construct large portions of a building on the ground, where it is safer and simpler, and then lifting them into place rather than doing all of the construction aloft. Tower cranes are increasingly used in Asia where construction has taken off in the 1990s. The biggest disadvantage of tower cranes is that once they are erected, they are very expensive and cumbersome to move to a new location.

MINING EQUIPMENT

The most gigantic, enormous, monstrous, colossal, and gargantuan of all heavy equipment is used for mining. The onset of mass society, particularly after World War II, has pushed the need for more and more energy resources and raw materials to fuel the seemingly insatiable appetite of modernity. This has meant digging deeper and searching farther afield for ever-increasing amounts of coal, iron, copper, and hundreds of other types of material.

And that requires big machinery—stupendously big, as big as buildings with buckets the size of houses and engines the size of trucks. Many of these machines are built and designed for specific mines. They are so large that trains, barges, and tractor-trailer trucks are required to bring all the pieces to the site and build the machines. It can take as long as three years to erect one of these machines. Once built, draglines, giant dump trucks, bucket wheel excavators, and other stripping shovels are operated 24 hours a day to maximize their use.

An unusual photographic exposure of a dragline at work in a coal mine offers a surrealistic display of the machine where the bucket loads and unloads its material.

BIG BRUTUS

The power plant built to provide the electricity to power Big Brutus could generate enough electricity to supply energy for a town of 15,000 people.

ABOVE: *Costing $6.5 million to build in 1963, Big Brutus was one of the first giant electric stripping shovels. The 160-foot-tall machine worked a Kansas coal mine for more than a decade. Today, it is the only giant stripping shovel open to the public.*

FACING PAGE, TOP: *A modern stripping shovel still has the same basic components as the original Otis Steam Excavator: a boom, a bucket, pulleys, and an engine.*

In its prime, Big Brutus was among the biggest of the big and a pioneering piece of machinery. Today, it is a museum, a relic of the past, and a monument to the coal-mining industry. Big Brutus is also the only giant stripping shovel open to the public.

Built in 1963 by Bucyrus-Erie Company, it took 150 railroad cars to haul 9.3 million pounds of machinery to southeastern Kansas, and it required 52 men to piece together the Bucyrus-Erie 1850-B Electric Shovel for the Pittsburg & Midway Coal Mining Company over the course of a year.

Dubbed "Big Brutus" by superintendent Emil Sandeen, the machine is 160 feet tall, or as high as a 16-story building. It cost $6.5 million to build and required its own power plant to operate. In the last month of operation for Big Brutus, it cost $27,000 just for the electric bill.

Although Big Brutus is relatively modest in size compared with later generations of stripping shovels, this heavy equipment was the second-largest shovel in the world in the early 1960s, a time when surface mining was rapidly growing out of its infancy. Its job was to strip the earth above coal deposits in in southeastern Kansas. For 11 years, Big Brutus did its job very well 24 hours a day, 7 days a week, 52 weeks a year. All told, it uncovered more than 9 million tons of coal used for local electric power generation.

Big Brutus's bucket capacity is 90 cubic yards, large enough to hold 150 tons of dirt with a single scoop. That is enough dirt to fill three railroad cars. Powered by eight 500-horse-power motors, it took four $3\frac{1}{2}$-inch-thick cables to lift the dipper.

The machine is supported by four gigantic hydraulic jacks. The hydraulic oil was held in a 3,200-gallon tank. The jack's cylinders are $3\frac{1}{2}$ feet wide and $5\frac{1}{2}$ feet long. Each jack is connected to four pairs of crawlers that move Big Brutus at a normal speed of 0.2 miles an hour. Each pair of crawlers had a 250-horse-power motor. Every crawler tread weighed a ton. Despite the size of Big Brutus, its operating crew consisted of only three men.

Big Brutus was eventually laid low by economics and environmental concerns. Coal in southeastern Kansas is high in sulfur and thus causes a high level of pollution. With the advent of the environmental movement in the 1960s and early 1970s, the costs of uncovering and cleaning high-sulfur coal became prohibitive. Pittsburg & Midway shut down Big Brutus in April 1974.

For almost ten years it sat idle. While it no longer served a useful purpose, it attracted visitors from miles around fascinated by its sheer size. Vic Boccia, the son of an operator of Big Brutus, came up with the idea of turning the giant shovel into a museum. He worked with Lounell Bath, numerous other volunteers, and the Pittsburg & Midway Coal Mining Company to make the idea a reality. The company donated the shovel, the surrounding 16 acres in West Mineral, Kansas, and $100,000 to the nonprofit Big Brutus, Inc., to start the museum in 1984.

"We started out with a card table outside and a shack," says Betty Becker, manager of Big Brutus, Inc. "Today we've got a visitors center and more then 30,000 visitors a year. People just seem to like its size. It's just really huge."

Otis Steam Excavator

Today's gargantuan stripping shovels are descendents of the first mechanically operated excavating machine, the Otis Steam Excavator. Built in the 1830s by William Otis Smith to help with the excavation work needed to lay a railroad line through western Massachusetts, the device used steam power to lift a bucket that was swung with a boom handled by two men. It was pulled by a team of horses.

Tiny by modern standards, observers at the time gushed at its impact. The *Springfield Republican* wrote that it provided "a great saving of labor." Smith received a patent for the machine, sold several more and was hailed for relieving some of the backbreaking aspects of laying a railroad track. It "does the work of fifty men," reported the *Philadelphia Saturday Courier*.

Improvements were made on the steam shovel as the nineteenth century unfolded. Much larger models were soon built. Steam shovels played a major role in the growth of the rail industry, mining, and countless construction projects. The advent of the combustible engine eventually supplanted the steam-powered shovel, but today's gigantic shovels can trace their roots to Smith's obscure machine shop in Canton, Massachusetts.

THE STEAM EXCAVATING MACHINE.

THE CAPTAIN

The Marion 6360, affectionately dubbed "The Captain," was the world's heaviest mobile land machine, weighing in at a mind-boggling 28 million pounds. Built by the Marion Steam Shovel Company in 1965, the electric stripping shovel was bought for $15 million by Southwestern Illinois Coal Corporation for its Captain Mine near Percy, Illinois. Only one Marion 6360 was ever built.

The Captain's job was to both remove the overburden from the upper seam of coal and the parting, the dirt between the upper seam and a second seam of coal, a task it did very well. In 26 years of service, The Captain removed more than 800 million cubic yards of soil.

The machine was a monster. It stood 22 stories high. It had eight motors generating a total of 24,000 horsepower just for hoisting The Captain's bucket. The bucket, which weighed 165 tons empty, was 18 1/2 feet wide, 16 feet high, and 24 1/2 feet deep. Its 180-cubic-yard capacity could hold 270 tons of dirt. All told, there were 36 motors generating between 200 and 460 horsepower each.

The boom was 215 feet long and the dipper handle stretched 133 feet, giving it a cutting radius of 236 feet. The housing was 88 feet long and 74 feet wide. Standing on eight crawlers, the shovel had a 16-foot clearance that allowed normal-sized vehicles to travel underneath the machine. Each of the crawlers was 45 feet long, 16 feet high, and 10 feet wide. A single pad on the crawlers weighed 7,000 pounds. There were 42 pads per crawler.

Fire killed The Captain. In September 1991 a hydraulic line burst, spraying fluid over electric panels that ignited the blaze. Years of grease and oil fed the flames and made it difficult to douse the fire. Although engineers deemed The Captain salvagable, the shovel's owners decided to scrap the gigantic machine.

▲ The Captain's 180-cubic-yard bucket weighed 165 tons empty and had enough space to hold more than eight Dodge Grand Caravans. It was the largest bucket ever built for a shovel.

Weighing 28 million pounds, The Captain was the heaviest earthmoving machine ever built. The Marion Steam Shovel Company erected the mammoth electric stripping shovel for the Southwestern Illinois Coal Corporation in 1965 for $15 million. It worked in an Illinois coal mine until 1991 when a fire destroyed the giant machine, which was turned into scrap metal.

▲ The track for a single crawler on The Captain weighed about 300,000 pounds.

BIG MUSKIE

Weighing in at 27 million pounds and swinging the largest bucket ever made, Big Muskie is the largest walking dragline and the second-heaviest mobile land machine in world history. Central Ohio Coal Company, a subsidiary of American Electric Power, commissioned Bucyrus-Erie in 1966 to build an enormous version of its 4250 series of draglines for its Muskingum mine, from which the name "Big Muskie" was derived. The Captain, a stripping shovel made by Marion Steam Shovel Company, weighed 1 million pounds more.

It took three years to build Big Muskie at a cost of $25 million. More than 300 rail cars and 250 trucks carried parts from the company's South Milwaukee plant to build the monstrous machine near Zanesville, Ohio. When completed in May 1969, Big Muskie stood 222 feet high. It was 487½ feet from the back of the housing to the tip of the twin boom, or almost one-tenth of a mile, and 151 feet wide, or as wide as an eight-lane highway.

Big Muskie's outstanding feature is its bucket. It weighs 230 tons, even before picking up an ounce of dirt. It has the dimensions of a house, standing about 14 feet high, 27 feet wide, and 23 feet deep. Its typical load weighs 325 tons. The cables that hold it are 5 inches thick. A yard of cable weighs 150 pounds, more than most adult men can lift. More than 1,200 yards of cable were used to hoist the bucket. Because of its constant use, the BE 4250-W required three buckets to ensure that at least one was always available.

The machine's housing is 140 feet long, 120 feet wide, and 40 feet tall, which is about the size of a six-story building that covers a quarter of a block in New York City. A hydraulic walking system with two 65-foot shoes is on each side of Big Muskie. A single step lurches Big Muskie 14 feet forward. Its walking speed is 900 feet per hour.

Big Muskie was powered with 13,800 volts of electricity, enough juice to generate 62,900 horsepower, or roughly the equivalent of 1,000 large bulldozers. In spite of its size, it only took one person to operate Big Muskie, although an extensive crew was needed to maintain it.

For 22 years, Big Muskie removed overburden from the Muskingum mine. All told, it removed 608 million cubic yards of dirt, which is the rough equivalent of removing five square

miles of earth at a depth of 120 feet. It uncovered more than 20 million tons of coal.

In January 1991 Big Muskie was shut down. The Clean Air Act of 1990 compelled the Central Ohio Coal Company to reduce its tonnage. The company decided to retire Big Muskie because it was not as cost-effective to run as some of the smaller machines. Tentative plans are being made to open the Big Muskie up to the public as a museum, but those plans have not been finalized.

Big Muskie, built by Bucyrus-Erie in 1966, is the largest dragline ever constructed. It is as wide as an eight-lane highway, taller than a 20-story building, and almost a tenth of a mile long. Its bucket could hold 220 cubic yards, or enough material to fill a three-bedroom house. The machine worked the Muskingum mine in Ohio from 1969 to 1991 when the Central Ohio Coal Company decommissioned the dragline.

▲ Big Muskie's hoisting ropes have a maximum lifting capacity of 2 million pounds.

▲ Big Muskie's capacity for holding hydraulic fluid alone is 26,000 gallons for all aspects of the machine.

DRAGLINES

Two trends are driving the demand for giant dragline excavators. One is the world's growing and insatiable appetite for energy and minerals to power the needs of an expanding industrialized globe. The other is the enormous pressure to keep excavation costs down. Unfortunately for the mining industry, most of the shallow deposits have already been discovered, uncovered, and unearthed. This means that miners have to dig deeper than ever to reach their goal, and they have to do it as cheaply as possible. Draglines offer the cheapest way to accomplish that aim in many situations.

First built at the turn of the twentieth century, draglines have been used for excavating large amounts of soil, minerals, and other materials for almost 100 years. Employing a large metal bucket maneuvered by a system of cables mounted from a walking structure, draglines are typically used today to remove overburden from coal, phosphate, and other mineral deposits. The buckets typically range in size from less than 10 cubic yards to more than 150 cubic yards. The largest dragline bucket ever made was 220 cubic yards.

The advantage of draglines is that they can remove large amounts of soil and dump it at another location with a single action. It costs about half as much to remove overburden and expose mineral deposits with a dragline than to do the same job with a shovel-and-truck combination. Cost calculations typically range from 20 to 30 cents to move a cubic yard of overburden with a dragline versus 50 to 70 cents for the shovel-truck removal. The largest dragline buckets have a capacity that is three or more times greater than the largest shovels. It also takes only two people to operate a dragline, whereas it requires a handful of truck drivers and a shovel operator for a shovel-truck combination. On the other hand, shovel-truck combinations are more flexible and are usually preferred for copper and iron mines where the minerals are separated.

John Page of Page and Schnable in Chicago invented in 1904 the first dragline excavator mounted on a rail track for a canal-building project in Illinois. The concept quickly caught on in the United States, and draglines were used for a wide variety of earthmoving projects. In 1913, Oscar J. Martinson of the Monighan Machine Corporation patented the first "walking" dragline that moved on giant metal feet similar to pontoons. The basic concept of draglines has not changed significantly since then, although many improvements have resulted in making them larger and more efficient. The development of more versatile and precise hydraulic shovels narrowed the range of uses for draglines, however, and the largest draglines now are usually used in mines.

These draglines are what are called *life-of-mine assets*. They are designed for specific mines and are intended to last as long as 30 or 40 years. It typically takes 3 years to design and build the largest draglines and costs as much as $35-$40 million. Draglines work on top of the ground, sitting above the area that is being excavated. Typically, draglines operate by digging "parallel cuts" to uncover the minerals below and dumping the material to one side of the cut. After removing the soil, the coal or mineral deposit is removed. Having completed a cut, the dragline then digs a new cut parallel to the old and dumps the overburden into the now mineral-free hole.

The depth of the cut depends on the length and angle of the boom. The largest booms are 420 feet long. In a typical example, a 360-foot boom positioned at a 35-degree angle (the range is usually between 30 and 38 degrees) has an operating radius of 331 feet, a digging depth of 200 feet, and a dumping height of 137 feet. The optimum boom length, bucket size, and angle are determined on a mine-by-mine basis by engineers. The largest manufacturers of draglines are all in the United States: Marion Steam Shovel Company, Bucyrus International, and P&H Mining Equipment.

A large dragline bucket dumps its load at a coal mine as the sun sets in the background.

LEFT: The view of a dragline removing overburden from a coal mine from an operator's perspective. Draglines sit above the material that is being removed. Typically, they dump the excavated material to the side and make extended cuts into the ground. When a new cut is made, it is often done parallel to the old one so that the overburden is dumped into the empty cut.

ABOVE, INSET: A P & H 9020 Walking Dragline at work in Australia. Note the two men by their car to the left of the giant dragline. The cable running into the rear of the machine supplies the dragline with electric power. The boom is longer than the length of a football field.

ABOVE: Draglines offer a very cost-effective way of moving huge amounts of material a relatively short distance. Here a walking dragline clears the overburden at a sulfur mine. Under certain conditions, draglines can cost half as much as using trucks and shovels to remove overburden.

LEFT: Mining companies are employing draglines with bigger and bigger booms to dig deeper into the ground. The longer the boom on a dragline, the greater its reach.

BELOW: A dragline dumps its load of overburden. It can take as long as three years and cost up to $40 million to build the largest draglines.

BOTTOM: A walking dragline removes overburden to expose the coal seam at a Wyoming coal mine. Draglines are life-of-mine assets, meaning that they are usually built for specific mines and work the mine until all of the valuable materials are removed. Properly maintained, they can last as long as 30 or 40 years.

▲ It costs as much as $30,000 a month to provide electricity to electric mining shovels. The power is supplied through a 2-inch-thick extension cord that can be as long as half a mile.

Stripping Shovels

ABOVE: An electric mining shovel prepares to dump a load of dirt into a truck bed from a gold mine quarry. At any time a shovel like this will consume more than 300 times as much electricity as a typical household.

▲ Hydraulic excavators, which are much more efficient and less costly to operate, have largely replaced electric mining shovels except for the largest machines.

▲ With the recent introduction of 300-ton mining trucks, some people in the industry expect that the size of electric mining shovels may once again increase. The goal of these shovels is to be able to fill a single hauling truck in three passes.

ABOVE: Stripping shovels almost always work in tandem with a team of mining dump trucks that remove the dirt and material to another location. Here an excavator drops its load in an iron ore mine.

Introduced in 1978, the P&H 5700 series is the world's largest two-crawler mining shovel. Weighing 2,000 tons or more with the capacity to hold dippers as large as 90 cubic yards, each crawler is more than 45 feet long and almost 10 feet wide. The electrically powered shovel has also been used as a dredge.

There are only three of the machines in operation: two in Australia and one in West Virginia. A fourth one is submerged in the ocean off the coast of Denmark, a victim of high seas in 1996. The P&H 5700—built by P&H Mining Equipment, a subsidiary of Harnischfeger Industries Company—is in some ways too big for the industry.

Mining companies have generally prefered smaller, less costly shovels that can fill a standard 240-ton dump truck with three passes in less than 90 seconds. It takes three passes with a 5700 to fill the same truck. The last P&H 5700 made sold for about $9 million, or about 50 percent more than those in the P&H 4100 series, which are pretty hefty machines themselves. P&H Mining has manufactured more than 70 mining shovels in the 4100 series with dippers ranging in size from 40 to 80 cubic yards. A single bucket on a 4100 shovel can hold 85 tons of dirt.

Nevertheless, improvements in tire technology have created the opportunity to create even bigger giant dump trucks, so there may be a revived interest in the P&H 5700 shovel. The other major manufacturers of loading shovels are Bucyrus International, Inc. and The Marion Power Shovel Company.

Tough, durable, and relatively inexpensive compared to the more imposing draglines, these types of shovels can be applied to a variety of uses including removing overburden, digging shattered rock, and excavating copper and iron ore directly. P&H Mining claims that some of its electric mining shovels are more than 30 years old, adding that properly maintained a shovel should last at least 20 years.

The electric power consumed to operate a two-crawler mining shovel is at least 300 times what a typical household uses. The P&H 4100 shovel is usually supplied by 7,200 volts of electricity with a half-mile, two-inch-thick extension cord. Working 450 hours per month, it will consume 430,000 kilowatts at the cost of about $30,000. A typical house with electric heating is rated for 240 volts and uses 1,500 kilowatts.

ABOVE: *An electric mining shovel can hold as much as 85 tons of dirt in its bucket. It typically takes 90 seconds for a shovel to make three passes and fill a 240-ton dump truck.*

ABOVE: *Drawing of a P&H 5700 shows the basic components of an electric stripping shovel's digging attachment. The boom for this shovel is 90 feet long.*

LEFT: *The largest two-crawler electric mining shovel ever made was the P&H 5700. The machine, however, was in fact too big for the industry and only four were sold. One of them was converted into a dredge for excavation work in the North Sea along the Danish coast. Rough waters, however, destroyed the $9 million shovel.*

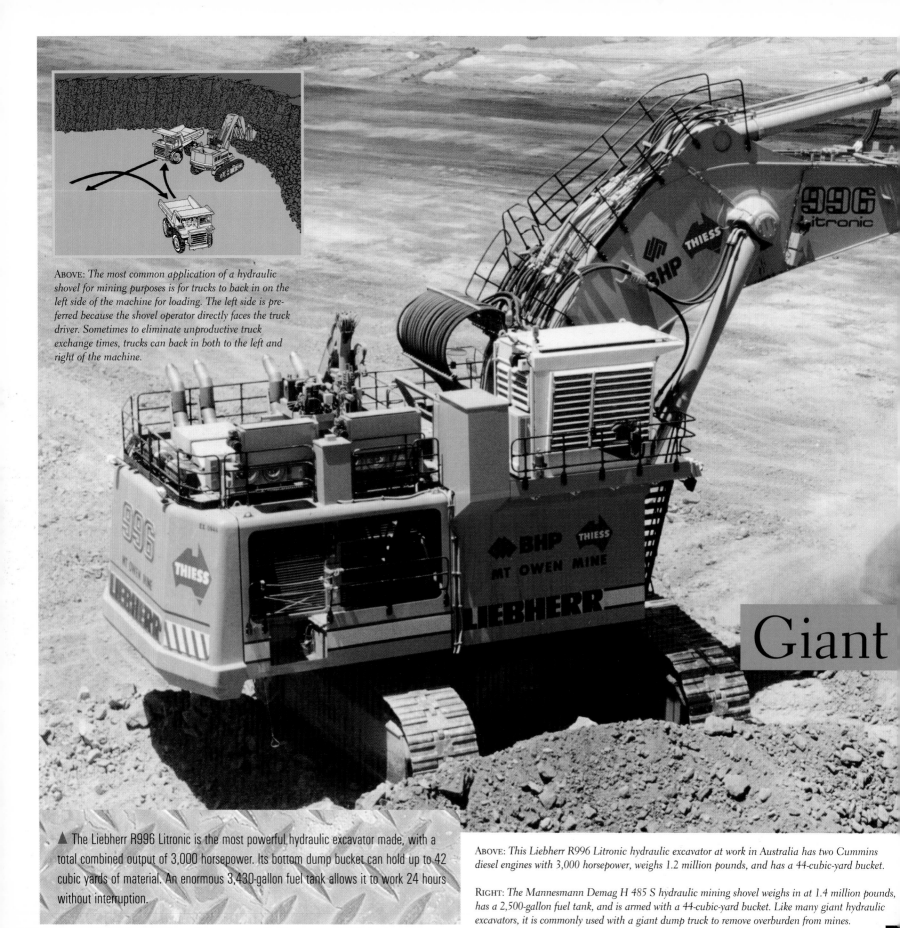

ABOVE: *The most common application of a hydraulic shovel for mining purposes is for trucks to back in on the left side of the machine for loading. The left side is preferred because the shovel operator directly faces the truck driver. Sometimes to eliminate unproductive truck exchange times, trucks can back in both to the left and right of the machine.*

Giant

▲ The Liebherr R996 Litronic is the most powerful hydraulic excavator made, with a total combined output of 3,000 horsepower. Its bottom dump bucket can hold up to 42 cubic yards of material. An enormous 3,430-gallon fuel tank allows it to work 24 hours without interruption.

ABOVE: *This Liebherr R996 Litronic hydraulic excavator at work in Australia has two Cummins diesel engines with 3,000 horsepower, weighs 1.2 million pounds, and has a 44-cubic-yard bucket.*

RIGHT: *The Mannesmann Demag H 485 S hydraulic mining shovel weighs in at 1.4 million pounds, has a 2,500-gallon fuel tank, and is armed with a 44-cubic-yard bucket. Like many giant hydraulic excavators, it is commonly used with a giant dump truck to remove overburden from mines.*

ike their smaller counterparts, giant hydraulic excavators have become increasingly popular because of their relatively low cost, fast speed, and high productivity. They are usually used in mines for digging and removing dirt and minerals. The largest hydraulic excavator is the Komatsu Demag H485S, a 1.4-million-pound excavator equipped with a 44-cubic-yard bucket and two massive engines that generate 3,590 horsepower.

Improvements in hydraulics over the last several years allowed companies such as Orenstein & Koppel (O&K), Liebherr, and Mannesmann Demag (recently acquired by Komatsu) to build bigger and bigger excavators that can be used for mining purposes. Electric mining shovels and draglines rely on gears to maneuver, creating friction and inefficiency. Because hydraulics is a nonfriction source of power, it is a more effective way of lifting and moving heavy materials. Although the largest hydraulic excavators are smaller than the largest electric shovels, they are usually faster and less costly to operate on a per-ton basis. It typically takes a giant hydraulic excavator about 25 seconds to complete a load-lift-dump-and-return cycle. Although they can be used for 40,000 hours or more, if properly maintained, they tend not to last as long as the bigger, more expensive mining shov-

formance. The Liebherr's 3,000-horsepower capacity makes it the most powerful shovel in its class. The acquisition of the WISEDA giant trucks by Liebherr in 1996 allowed the company to market its shovel in combination with 190- and 240-ton trucks. It takes four passes with the R996 to fill a 240-ton truck.

The dimensions of the Komatsu Demag H485S are immense. The bucket alone weighs 110,000 pounds, which is more than the combined weight of all the players on ten NFL football teams. It is 18 feet wide and typically lifts up to 60 tons of material. The machine itself is 60 feet long, 35 tall, and 18 feet wide, giving it the approximate dimensions of a three-story apartment building. The fuel tank is 10 feet long, 6 feet wide, and 10 feet tall, and can hold 2,510 gallons of fuel. The hydraulic oil tank's capacity is 2,100 gallons (a typical whirlpool bath holds about 50 gallons of water). The operator

Hydraulic Excavators

els and draglines that may have lives of 100,000 hours or longer. Which type of shovel works best in a mine depends on the material being handled, the mine's layout, the life span of the project, and other factors.

In 1954, Demag built the first hydraulic excavator. The French company Poclain unveiled the first fully hydraulic mining excavator in 1971, the 151-ton EC1000. In 1986, Demag introduced the H485, which is still the largest hydraulic excavator available. Liebherr introduced in 1996 a smaller but still massive R996 Litronic, a 1.2-million-pound shovel complete with intelligent electronics to monitor, regulate, and control all its key systems for top per-

of the excavator has to climb almost 23 feet to get to the cab, where there is a commanding view 26 feet above the ground. The tractor crawlers are 26 feet long and 5 feet wide. The massive machine's top speed is 1.46 miles per hour.

ABOVE: *Caterpillar's largest hydraulic excavator is the 5230. It weighs 330 tons, carries a 22-cubic-yard bucket, and boasts a 50-foot reach.*

Rotary Blast Drills

The amount of continuous downward force applied to the largest rotary blast drill bits is 150,000 pounds with compressed air clearing the fragmented particles at a rate Éof up to 3,600 cubic feet per minute. The drills can dig holes as wide as 22 inches and as deep as 130 feet.

Relatively small in size, rotary blast drills pack a powerful punch and clear the way for larger earthmoving machines. Whether the task is mining, removing compacted rock, or blowing up a field of iron ore, holes need to be drilled to place explosive materials that will fragment rocks, ore, and dirt that are too hard for ordinary excavating machines. That is the job of the rotary blast drill.

The largest rotary blast drills are used for mining operations. Mounted on large crawlers, they look like a cross between a mobile trailer home and a small offshore oil rig. The business end of the machine is the drill, which consists of three basic components to pierce the earth with a hole as wide as 22 inches. One element is the rotary drill itself, a three-headed conical bit that turns, similar to a gargantuan household drill pushing the earth below out of the way. The second element is the pull-down force that applies pressure onto the bit to facilitate the drilling process just as a person might lean into his or her household drill to speed up the job. The force is applied with hydraulics from a rugged mast and frame on the drill. Finally, compressed air is forced into the deepening hole to blow out the fragmented pieces being drilled with jetlike force. The machine is run from the operator's cab with sophisticated controls that also provide monitoring and diagnostic analysis for all the machine's mechanical, electrical, main air, and hydraulic systems.

How much pressure is applied, the speed of the rotation, the amount of time it takes to dig a hole, and several other factors are determined by the type of material being penetrated. Iron ore is fantastically dense, three times as hard as sidewalk cement. It takes a drill many times longer to drill into iron ore than into a softer material such as limestone. The P & H 120 A drill, for example, will drill a hole up to 22 inches in diameter 80 feet into the ground, applying force of up to 75 tons. The machine's list price is $2 million and it has an estimated life span of about 20 years. The drill will typically make a series of holes in precisely distanced locations and load them with explosives. The explosives are detonated in very rapid sequence, creating a wavelike mass of fragmented stone and dust. Many drills are now using global positioning systems (GPS) to place the holes. Accurate to within an inch or two, GPS removes the need for a surveying team to direct the operator.

There is also an entire class of smaller rock drills used for smaller-scale operations. Crawler-mounted blast hole drills operate under a similar principle but are smaller and have the drills attached to a track-mounted crawler with a single or double boom. Some rock drills are designed to mount on excavators and backhoe loaders. And just as their larger cousins have developed new and sophisticated systems, they, too, are undergoing technological changes to improve efficiencies. Manufacturers have applied systems, such as antijam devices and load-sensing pumps, that allow drills to monitor rock conditions as they work and adjust accordingly. The machines typically drill holes between 1½ and 6 inches in diameter to depths of up to 100 feet. Prices vary from $300,000 to $600,000.

ABOVE: *A large rotary blast drill is in operation while other machines remove coal below. The largest crawler drills weigh more than 180 tons and can dig holes as much as 65 feet deep with a single drill pipe pass. Explosions are often set at the same time every day for safety reasons.*

LEFT: *An Ingersoll-Rand crawler drill at work. The wear and tear on crawler drills is significant. Almost half the operating expense of blast drills is for new parts. Labor represents less than a third of the average hourly expense.*

FACING PAGE: *A powerful rotary blast drill prepares a pattern of blast holes on a "bench" in an Arizona copper mine. When the pattern of 16-inch-wide, 60-feet-deep holes is completed, explosives will be loaded and detonated. The shattered ore bench is then ready for large excavators to move in and load the broken ore into 240-ton-capacity haul trucks.*

FACING PAGE, INSET: *Two crawler drills prepare to shatter a section of this mine. A stripping shovel removes material in the background. The scattered rocks in the foreground are almost certainly the remains of an earlier explosion.*

⚠ Hourly ownership and repair expenses for crawler-mounted rotary blast hole drills range from $160 to $300. The average monthly ownership and repair expense is more than $28,000.

onsider the tire on a giant dump truck. A 240-ton dump truck is carried by six tires, each 12 feet in diameter and weighing 4 tons. That is heavier than three Ford Taurus cars and taller than two full-grown men standing on the other's shoulders. That's just one tire.

Giant dump trucks aren't as big as a house; they're bigger. Costing $1.5 million and up, these behemoths are so heavy and so large that they are not allowed on public roads. It usually takes at least six semi-trucks to carry on-site all the parts required to build a 240-ton dump truck.

Once pieced together, giant dump trucks typically serve a simple role in open-pit mining. Their job is to carry dirt, coal, iron, phosphate ore, and rocks filled with bits of gold, silver, taconite, and other minerals back and forth in mining facilities.

Open-pit mining requires the removal of *overburden*, a layer of earth covering the valued minerals as deep as 150 feet below the ground.

ABOVE: *A giant by the standards of 1955, this 50-ton dump truck doubled as a swimming pool in a publicity stunt in Chicago to promote the new record-setting machine. Today, it would take six to seven times as much water to fill the carriage of the largest dump trucks.*

Giant Dump Trucks

▲ It typically costs $120 an hour to operate a 240-ton dump truck. Tire maintenance alone costs about $25 an hour. Fuel and lube costs represent between 30 and 35 percent of the operating costs.

▲ The fuel tank in a 240-ton truck carries 1,000 gallons. Giant 240-ton dump trucks typically consume 5 gallons of gas per mile. The maximum speed for most giant dump trucks is 35 miles per hour.

▲ The average life of a giant dump truck is 15 years during which time it will be in operation for about 80,000 hours.

This makes for a lot of dirt that has to be removed. The advent of environmental management guidelines in many countries has also meant that the excavated material must be returned to refill the gaping hole when the mining work is done.

Out of that need was born the modern giant dump truck. The bigger the dump truck, the fewer the loads needed to be carried back and forth and the less expensive the task. Thus, the demand for bigger and bigger trucks.

The first supersized dump trucks designed for open-pit mining were built in the late 1950s. Initially carrying loads of between 20 and 30 tons, their capacities quickly grew to 65 tons. After overcoming constraints in the capacity of transmissions, the first 100-ton truck was built in 1965. By 1970, a 150-ton truck was on the market, and in 1982 WISEDA introduced the first 200-ton dump truck, which served as the model for the 240-ton truck, the industry standard for many years.

Two companies dominate the giant dump truck market (100 tons and larger): Caterpillar and Komatsu. These two combined sold 75 percent of the more than 750 giant dump trucks delivered in 1996. The other major players are Euclid, Unit Rig, and Libherr, which recently acquired WISEDA.

Caterpillar is the only one of the three that manufactures all components of its trucks, ranging in size from 35 to 240 tons. Using a mechanical-drive system as opposed to a diesel-electric one, Caterpillar claims to have better fuel economy and fewer maintenance problems than do its competitors.

Komatsu Dresser Company has perhaps the most giant dump trucks in the mine pits. Its Haulpak division has long been a leader in the field, developing several new technologies, including an exhaust system that heats

LEFT: *Working in its natural environment, a 240-ton truck prepares to haul overburden from an open-mining pit. It will take the stripping shovel 90 seconds to fill the truck with three bucket loads of earth.*

FACING PAGE: *A Liebherr 240-ton dump truck makes the company's oversized pickup truck look like a Tonka toy in comparison.*

FACING PAGE, INSET: *The view from the driver's seat of a Liebherr giant dump truck is surprisingly similar to an ordinary truck—except that it is 20 feet above the ground.*

LEFT: *Mining for oil, a mechanic is dwarfed by the size of a 150-ton truck as he checks its oil at an Arizona copper mine.*

BELOW: *Two 240-ton Caterpillar trucks work in tandem to carry overburden at an Idaho gold mine.*

▲ The equipment used to maintain a giant dump truck is almost as impressive as the trucks themselves. Superjacks weighing 14,500 pounds can lift 90 tons of machinery off the ground, specially designed transporters can carry giant dump truck parts that weigh up to 15 tons, and self-propelled booms can lift and maneuver large components weighing as much 4,500 pounds.

the body of the dump truck, the V-shaped dump body, and most recently computer-driven trucks and the record-shattering 300-ton Komatsu 930E.

Komatsu 930E Dump Truck

The biggest truck in the world is the Komatsu 930E, a 310-ton behemoth that is the first of what is expected to be a new generation of even more gigantic giant dump trucks. The truck is so big that the 2,500-horsepower engine alone (without any oil, water, or fuel) weighs the same as four Jeep Cherokees. The

16-cylinder engine's crankcase holds 55 gallons of oil, its radiator 195 gallons of water, and its tank 1,200 gallons of fuel.

The truck is almost 24 feet high, 50 feet long, and almost 27 feet wide, which is to say it is as tall and wide as a two-story, three-bedroom house, and as long as a basketball court is wide. The truck's V-shaped body has a 241-cubic-yard capacity and can hold 310 tons of material. The floor consists of two sheets of 3/4-inch-thick tensile-strength steel and can withstand up to 150,000 pounds of pressure per square inch. Empty, the truck weighs

410,000 pounds; loaded, slightly more than 1 million pounds. The trucks are usually built on-site from parts made in Peoria, Illinois, unless the destination is accessible by water. Then the trucks are transported on a barge.

Before the driver can start the 16-cylinder engine, he or she first has to climb a 14-foot ladder to reach the cab. The tires are 4 feet wide and about 10 feet tall. Multiple disc brakes apply up to 2,500 pounds per square inch of pressure on the tires to stop. By way of comparison, a house sitting on the ground exerts 1,500 pounds per square inch of pres-

sure. Each tire costs $70,000. Six tires are used for each truck. The listed price for the truck (minus the tires) is $3.6 million.

The Komatsu 930E came on to the market in 1996. The company says the truck has been selling well. Both Caterpillar and Liebherr Mining Truck, Inc., have announced plans to follow Komatsu's lead and will build similar trucks. Liebherr is developing a 320-ton payload hauler, the KL-2620. Caterpillar is working on a 340-ton truck.

"They are going to keep getting bigger," says William Bontemps of Komatsu America

Komatsu 930E Giant Dump Truck

International. "The economies of scale keeps pushing the size up. I don't know when it's going to stop."

To keep operating costs down, mining companies are turning to larger trucks as more efficient ways to increase the amount of material moved with less fuel and fewer operators. But making bigger trucks isn't as simple as increasing the dimensions. Giant dump trucks had reached a plateau of about 240 tons for several years. Several technological and economic barriers stood in the way of bigger trucks. There were problems with matching the engine's horsepow-

er with the size of the machine, coming up an appropriate electric drive system and developing tires to carry the giant machines. A new AC drive system that better utilized the horsepower represented one breakthrough. The development of stronger materials for the tires was another. Finally, there had to be a willingness to invest money into machines that would make the parts and tires for the new, even more giant trucks. Financial pressure on mining companies has allowed all of the elements come together to build giant trucks such as the Komatsu 930E and even bigger ones in the future.

▲ The dimensions of the Komatsu 930E truck's body (more than 29 feet long, 26 feet wide, and 8 feet deep) are approximately the same as the length and width of a squash court.

The Komatsu 930E is the biggest truck in the world, capable of carrying 310 tons in its carriage. Both Caterpillar and Liebherr, however, are planning to build even bigger trucks in the near future.

BUCKET WHEEL

Bucket wheel excavators are particularly well suited for soft and loose materials. The preponderance of ledge and large rocks in North America has prevented their widespread use in the United States.

ABOVE: *Large by almost any other standard, this modestly sized bucket wheel excavator moves on rails. This picture clearly shows all the basic components of the machine: the superstructure that holds the booms, conveyor systems, and hoisting winch; the booms that hold the buckets and serve as a counterweight; the conveyor belts to carry materials; and the bucket wheel.*

ABOVE, INSET: *The power and size of the bucket wheel excavator's scoops are clear in this photograph of a machine at work in the oil tar sands of Alberta, Canada.*

LEFT: *A German soft-coal mine pit with a large bucket wheel excavator at the bottom that appears to have had the bucket wheel removed. Nevertheless, the evidence of the machine's work is clear to see as the machine chewed layers of coal out of the earth as it descended into the ground.*

EXCAVATORS

Of all the world's mobile machines, the giant bucket wheel excavator is perhaps the most impressive in terms of both its size and its complexity. Starting with its wheel of buckets that ceaselessly remove soil and ending with the sheer size of the giant machine, the bucket wheel excavator is a marvel.

The concept is simple, even if the design is not. A large circular wheel studded with buckets spins around scooping piles of dirt, coal, or other material and dumps it onto a conveyor system that carries and sorts the material according to the needs of the enterprise.

Most often seen in open-pit mining operations (especially in Germany), bucket wheel excavators are also used for digging canals and for projects requiring the removal of large amounts of dirt. Bucket wheel excavators are not used very often in the United States because the ground is often too hard and possesses too many large rocks or ledge.

In its most basic form, the bucket wheel excavator has five central components: (1) the undercarriage and crawlers that hold up and move the machine; (2) the superstructure in the center that holds the booms, conveyor systems, and hoisting winch; (3) the booms that hold the bucket wheel, the counterweight to the working end of the machine, and the conveyor system that removes the debris; (4) the conveyor belts that carry and remove the excavated materials; and (5) the bucket wheel that does the actual digging.

The largest bucket wheel excavators have buckets the size of cars, typically 8 to 10.7 cubic yards apiece. Each wheel has between 10 and 24 buckets. The harder the material being dug, the greater the number of buckets used. The speed of the wheel depends on the conditions. An extended boom positions the wheel to remove materials from the ground. As the material is excavated, the machine moves the wheel into a new position to continue the process. The larger machines are operated by a single operator and a crew of four attendants. Smaller ones only require two people.

The largest machines are used in the brown coal mines of Germany. Weighing close to 14,800 short tons (13,500 metric tons), their 70-plus-foot diameter bucket wheels remove 3,260,000 cubic yards of material a day. Several bucket wheel excavators work the mine pits, which can be as deep as 800 feet, removing 100 million metric tons of lignite a year.

It takes three years from the beginning of the design to the machine's manufacture and then to its being assembled on-site. It will last 40 years if properly maintained. The cost is up to Deutsch Mark 200 million (rate of exchange: $1 equals Deutsch Mark 1.7) to build one. Krupp Fördertechnik and MAN Tákraf, both German companies, make most of the world's bucket wheel excavators. Although there are standard bucket wheel excavators, many of the machines are designed for specific projects. Today, bucket wheel excavators are used across the globe, including India, Africa, Australia, and Europe.

ABOVE: *The giant Krupp Bucket Wheel Excavator 288 weighs a massive 29 million pounds and is longer than two football fields. Its 18 rotating buckets can remove more than 250,000 cubic yards of soil per day. Fifteen crawlers are used to move the giant machine.*

LEFT: *A bituminous coal stacker/reclaimer works the coal docks in Ashtabula, Ohio. Bucket wheel excavators are rarely used in the United States as they are not effective at digging North America's hard and rocky soils.*

The biggest bucket wheel excavators will remove more than 320,000 cubic yards of material a day, or a hunk of earth that has the dimensions of a football field and is 180 feet deep.

RIGHT: *A bucket wheel excavator in Western Australia stockpiles iron ore in Port Hedland.*

BELOW: *A bucket wheel excavator is used as a stacker/reclaimer at the McDuffie Island Coal Handling Facility in Mobile, Alabama. This is a fairly small machine, at least by bucket wheel excavator standards.*

BELOW: *A large bucket wheel excavator at work at an opencast coal mine at night in Kazakhstan. The wheel cuts into the coal seam and deposits the coal onto a conveyor belt on the boom. The coal is in this way carried from the face and loaded into trucks. Waste material, such as the topsoil and underlying strata, are later replaced in the mine.*

A Short History of Bucket Wheel Excavators

Leonardo da Vinci is the first person known to have applied to paper the idea of using mounted buckets on a wheel for digging purposes. A similar concept had been used since ancient times for waterwheels in irrigation systems.

Until the nineteenth century wheel excavators and water wheels were driven by wind, water, human, or animal power. The invention of the steam engine, however, opened up new possibilities. The first continuously operating steam-driven bucket excavator was used in railroad construction in France. Later, in the 1860s, bucket wheel excavators were used with great success by French engineers to dig the Suez Canal.

The next fifty years saw an extended series of patents, new inventions, and developments, and in 1916 the first rail-mounted bucket wheel excavator was built to remove overburden from German coal mines. Nine years later, the "Autoschaufler" entered German mines. Built on crawlers, six buckets dug the earth and dumped it onto a conveyor belt, which carried it a short distance to an unloading point where it was placed in a hauler.

The development of electrical drive technologies allowed German engineers in the 1930s to build much more complicated and practical machines to remove large amounts of material. Several machines were built, forerunners to today's giant machines. World War II stunted the development of the machines, but beginning in the 1950s new welding techniques, larger engines and experience allowed German mining companies to construct the larger and increasingly sophisticated bucket wheel excavators of today.

There have been four generations of giant bucket wheel excavators. First, in the 1950s, machines with an average capacity of 80,000 cubic yards per day were manufactured. Starting in 1960, a new generation of excavators with a capacity of 130,000 cubic yards was conceived. Twenty years later, the first of the giant 260,000-cubic-yard-per-day machines was built. In 1983, a 320,000-cubic-yard-per-day machine followed.

ABOVE: An early bucket wheel excavator at work in the Culebra Cut in the Panama Canal. The success of bucket wheel excavators in digging the Suez Canal gave French engineers the confidence to think they could dig a similar canal through Panama. But they were wrong. The machines were not up to the harsh conditions of the Central American jungle nor the hard and muddy earth, which proved to much tougher to dig than the sands of the desert. Ultimately, the machines played a supplementary role in the successful American effort.

GERMAN MINING RECLAMATION

Giant spreaders used in mine reclamation projects can dump as much as 135,000 cubic yards of soil in a day, or the equivalent of laying 6 feet of dirt onto 13 football fields.

ABOVE: *A spreader dumps a 7-foot layer of topsoil in Germany's Rhineland area as part of a massive mine reclamation project. The spreader, which is positioned low to the ground for accurate placement of the soil, can unload as much as 135,000 cubic yards of soil per day. Tractors in the background level the soil. To avoid soil compaction, engineers are very careful in selecting relatively light machines for the leveling.*

LEFT: *A German farmer checks the progress of wheat on a recultivated mine dump. The large machine in the background is a spreader used for laying thick layers of dirt onto the ground. Such spreaders are very similar to bucket wheel excavators used to dig the mines, but they do not have the earthmoving bucket wheel attachments. It typically takes 5 to 7 years for agricultural land to be completely recultivated.*

As impressive and gigantic as mining equipment is, it can also be—from an environmental perspective—incredibly destructive. Draglines, stripping shovels, bucket wheel excavators, and other machines take huge hunks of earth out of the ground, disturbing nature's work in violent ways. From the air, an open mine looks a lot like an open wound. Furthermore, after having its mineral wealth removed, the mined property has literally had its value stripped away. Increasing concern about the environmental impact of open mines, as well as the potential value of restoring mining regions, has led to a growing effort to reclaim opencast mines for productive use.

Far and away, the most far-reaching reclamation efforts have taken place in the German brown-coal mining regions. Dating back to the eighteenth century when a local bishop proclaimed that miners would have to reclaim their mines for productive use, Germans have reclaimed tens of thousands of acres to productive use. Formerly desolate areas have been restored as farmland, forests, lakes, and even villages. Much of the reclamation process is overseen and directed by a semiprivate company called the Rheinische AG.

Historically, Germany has had to look within its own country for its natural resources. While other European countries built empires abroad, Germany was late to "the game," and after World War I the nation lost those colonies it had acquired. Germany found its fossil fuels by digging for coal on its own land. As an industrial country, it needed a lot of coal, and this meant excavating giant mine pits. Close to 400,000 acres of German land have been mined. Rather than simply let these desolated areas just sit unused, starting in about 1920 the country undertook an ambitious recultivation program, often using the same types of equipment that had distorted the landscape to restore it to productive use. The most successful recultivation has taken place in the Rhineland brown-coal mining area.

The reclamation of mined areas is a complicated process. It is not simply a question of dumping loads of dirt on top of the mined areas and letting nature take its course. Several factors are considered including the future use of the land, drainage, regional planning, groundwater conditions, geological conditions, and, most important, the quality of the recultivated soil. The soil is acquired from active mines. Topsoil and certain types of soil that are found underground can be used for recultivation. Different mixes of different types of soil can provide a reliable foundation from which to recultivate farmland and forests, and reclaim lakes and land for other uses. Not surprisingly, farmland requires the most biologically rich soil. Selecting the right soil material and applying it correctly are the decisive factors in successful reclamation projects. Many recultivation projects have failed because the wrong types of soil were used or the process was done in an inappropriate way.

Soil compaction can be a major hindrance to reclamation efforts. The heavy weight of bulldozers can literally squeeze the life out of the soil below. To mitigate the impact of soil compaction, giant spreaders are used to lay thick layers of dirt onto the ground between 6 and 15 feet deep. Similar to bucket wheel excavators minus the buckets, they can dump as much as 135,000 cubic yards of topsoil per day. Giant conveyor belts are positioned fairly close to the ground to make sure the distribution is tightly controlled. The soil is often left to dry for a short time and then leveled by bulldozers or other machines with very low ground pressure.

The application of the tillable cultivated layer of soil, mostly consisting of loess or loam, is followed by 7 years of interim farming (usually the sowing and maintenance of alfalfa) that leads to the cultivation of main crops such as barley, wheat, rye, and vegetables. Properly done, agricultural recultivation can produce land with even higher yields than old farmland. In Germany's Neuss County, for example, the recultivated land in 1991 had higher or the equivalent yields of wheat, rye, barley, rape, and sugar beet. Forest recultivation takes longer to accomplish. By using native seeds and seedlings, however, experts have made it possible for a forest to become recognizable in as little as 20 years. Reforestation planners have become very creative, often combining multiple tree species, and even rare trees, as part of a new forest's mix. Ironically, the recultivated areas have become critical breeding grounds for the protection of endangered species.

RIGHT: *A water catchment pond on a reforested dump. Planners use diverse mixes of native plants to recreate forests on formerly desolate land. Some of the new forests harbor rare species and are used as recreational areas.*

About 40,000 acres in the Rhineland brown-coal mining region have been recultivated. Slightly more than half the reclaimed land is used for agriculture with the balance being covered in forests, lakes, settlements, and land used for other purposes. It typically takes 5 to 7 years for agricultural recultivation and 20 years for forest recultivation.

UNDERGROUND

A 3FCT Continuous Haulage Flexible Conveyor Train by Joy Mining Machinery can navigate 90-degree turns within the narrow confines of an underground mine. The machine can haul material at a rate of 16 tons per minute.

While sheer size and power distinguish the equipment used in open mining operations, the machinery used for underground mining is marked by the peculiarities of having to unearth huge amounts of material within the narrow confines of underground shafts. The heavy equipment used for underground mining accomplishes three basic tasks: loosening embedded coal, rocks, and other material; hauling it out of the mine; and supporting the earth above the mine shaft from collapsing onto workers below. The era of using a pick, a shovel, and wooden beams to perform these tasks is long gone, replaced by highly sophisticated and powerful machines.

Technology has been applied to underground mining, vastly improving miners' productivity. The number of workers in the mining industry in the United States dropped by more than 20 percent from 1987 to 1997, but the average worker's productivity soared. From 1990 to 1994 alone, productivity in coal mines grew close to 30 percent. The advances have come at a time when many of the easily accessible pockets of underground minerals have been tapped out and international competition has often driven commodity prices down.

The most important development in underground mining has been long-wall mining. Operated by a small crew of miners, the complex machine consists of two cylinder-shaped shearers studded with picks and chisels that run back and forth along a face of coal. The shearers can be up to 10 feet in diameter. Boulder-size chunks of coal fall onto a conveyor below, which removes the material. As the shearers do their work at a rate of up to 1,000 tons per hour, massively powerful hydraulic roof supports automatically creep forward, providing cover for the machines and workers. The roof supports, which can be as high as 20 feet, can hold 7,000 pounds per square inch or more. The machines are custom-made for different mining conditions. A typical long-wall system was sold by Joy Mining to South Blackwater Coal, Limited, in Australia. It consisted of one hundred fourteen 992-ton roof supports, a 656-foot-long armored face conveyor, and a 1,270-horsepower shearer. The long-wall systems continue to smash production records. In the early 1990s, the record monthly output of a long-wall system was about

▲ The dark and narrow passages of an underground mine make for some peculiar-looking equipment for underground mines. Drivers in shuttle cars will often lie down to fit inside the mine, and articulated conveyor trains are designed to negotiate 90-degree turns by bending their joints to navigate the turn.

CENTER: The studs and chisels of a continuous mining machine knock off blocks of coal and rock from the face of the mine. The machine is controlled by an attached box held by the operator.

ABOVE: Several hundred feet long, longwall systems consist of a series of powerful jacks that hold up the earth above and a conveyor system below that removes the debris as the cutterhead races back and forth.

MINING EQUIPMENT

500,000 tons. Five years later, the record was approaching 1 million tons per month. At Twentymile Coal Mine in Colorado, for example, it took a long-wall system a month to excavate a bed of coal 1,000 feet underground that was 8 feet high, 840 feet wide, and 3½ miles long.

While other types of underground mining equipment have less spectacular results, they provide extremely powerful and targeted digging capacity for working in tight spaces. Continuous mining machines, similar to cutterheads for tunneling (See "Tunneling Machines," page 84), crack mine faces with their massive cutter motors under the protection of overhead shields. Underground hauling equipment has to remove large amounts of material through the narrow and sometimes winding tunnel shafts. In addition to continuous conveyor belt systems, the equipment includes shuttle cars that are as low as 28 inches off the ground and articulated haulers that can carry 40,000 pounds of more material at speeds of 5 miles per hour or more. Perhaps the most extraordinary of hauling equipment, however, are the flexible conveyor trains. Mounted on wheels, they can be 500 feet or longer, are capable of negotiating 90-degree turns, and can move materials at a rate of 16 tons per minute moving 650 feet per minute.

ABOVE: A Joy Mining Machinery shuttle car is long in its width but short in height to fit through the low ceilings of a coal mine. Shuttle cars can be as low as 28 inches off the ground.

▲ A modern 1,200-horsepower longwall system will remove 30 million pounds or more of coal from a single mine in a day. The jacks that hold up earth can bear the weight of 1,000 tons of dirt.

ABOVE, LEFT INSET: The cutterhead of a longwall system is a fierce-looking set of reinforced studs, chisels, and picks that knock chunks of coal and rock off the mine's face.

ABOVE, CENTER INSET: A continuous miner is about to eat into a mine thousands of feet underground. The space is so small that the operator cannot stand.

ABOVE, RIGHT INSET: Superpowerful hydraulic roof supports hold thousands of tons of earth to protect workers inside the mines.

LEFT: A 4LS Longwall Shearer by Joy Mining Machinery in action. These types of machines remove 20,000 tons of material in a day.

They looked like bizarre riverboats stuck in the mud, but the gold dredges of Alaska represented one of the most ambitious endeavors taken by heavy machinery in their day. Beyond the scale of gold dredges was the scope of work preparing for excavation. Canals as long as 90 miles were built and acres of frozen muck were washed before a dredge could even begin work.

When gold was first discovered in Alaska around the turn of the twentieth century, thousands of prospectors armed with shovels, picks, ingenuity, and daring scoured the territory for gold. Before long most of the easy finds were mined. The more challenging work of finding and removing gold from remote locations in Alaska required bigger machinery, more resources, and greater staying power.

By the 1920s, the Fairbanks Exploration Company had emerged as the biggest and most efficient gold-mining operation in Alaska. After several ventures attempted with decidedly mixed results to dredge along and near Alaska's coasts, some of the more successful dredgers ventured to Fairbanks in the interior where there were known gold deposits. The problem was that the gold was buried in gravel beneath frozen muck as deep as 160 feet. But the Fairbanks Exploration Company, backed by big money from the eastern United States, was up to the task.

To even get to the point where a dredge could process the earth, giant hoses and to a lesser extent dragline shovels removed the muck. (One of the happy byproducts of this process was the uncovering of prehistoric animals such as saber-toothed tigers and woolly mammoth, which were brought to the American Museum of Natural History in New York City.) The immense amount of water needed for the task was supplied by canals built by the company. Having removed the muck, engineers then had to thaw the ground below by injecting hundreds of pipes every 16 to 32 feet and running water into the icy turf. The whole process was further complicated by Alaskan winters, which kept the dredging season to about 200 days.

Once the muck was removed and the ground below thawed, the dredges went to work. Fairbanks Exploration had eight dredges. The largest one, Dredge No. 10, was 167$\frac{1}{2}$ feet long and 74 $\frac{1}{4}$ feet wide. The dredges used bucket lines that removed the gold-laden soil at a rate of 22 buckets a minute. The size of the buckets ranged from 3 to 10 cubic feet.

The buckets carried their loads inside the dredge, and dumped the load into a rotating cylinder called a *trommel* that sifted the finer particles onto sorting bins known as *gold tables* below. Water then washed the fine sand and gold over *riffles*, shallow dips, which trapped the heavy gold particles. All the other materials—the dirt, gravel, sand, and water—were discharged out the back. The dredge moved forward as it dug out the earth in front of it. In a single season, a dredge might travel between 1,000 and 5,000 feet.

Alaskan gold dredges were at their peak in the late 1930s. The dredges, however, were shut down during World War II, and they never quite recovered afterward. By the 1960s, gold dredging was no longer economical, though some of the dredges were periodically used until 1994. Also, gold dredges devastated the landscape, leaving piles of discarded rubble in their wake, washing millions of tons of silt down unspoiled streams, and littering the countryside with chemicals, mercury, and other waste.

Today gold dredges are a memory. Gray Line of Alaska recently bought Gold Dredge No. 8 and opened it as a tourist attraction just north of Fairbanks. The four-story dredge, which was listed as a national historic landmark by the American Society of Mechanical Engineers, produced more than 7.5 million ounces of gold and had a 95 percent efficiency rating.

Top, INSET: *Gold Dredge No. 8 was one of eight large dredges used by the Fairbanks Exploration Company to mine the Alaskan interior around Fairbanks. The dredge had 66 buckets moving at a rate of 22 buckets per minute. It processed an average of 6,000 cubic yards of thawed muck a day. The dredge is now owned by Gray Line of Alaska as a tourist site.*

CENTER, INSET: *An old gold dredge in Nome, Alaska, is a typical example of the mining machines. Buckets on an extended boom would churn up the gold-laden earth and carry it inside the house where the dirt was separated from the gold dust. Having been processed, the valueless mud poured out the rear of the machine. The largest dredges processed an average of 10,000 cubic yards of earth a day.*

RIGHT: *Before the gold dredges did their work, teams of workers thawed vast amounts of frozen muck to uncover the gold below. The process was very labor-intensive and messy. Even before the arrival of the environmental movement in the 1960s, some observers criticized the harsh impact the mining had on Alaska's wildlife.*

MINING MASTODONS

Where the dredges, pounding, whine and scream,
And the rock goes in in an unending stream
And comes out at the end, a sourdough's dream
Of gold, gold, gold.

— NINA CRUNRINE, POETRY SOCIETY OF ALASKA

ABOVE: *The gold dredges of Alaska represented one of the most ambitious uses of heavy equipment in the early part of the twentieth century. The large and expensive dredges proved to be the most efficient way to mine for gold in Alaska's remote and harsh environment.*

At their height in the late 1930s and early 1940s, the gold dredges of Alaska were removing between 40,000 and 50,000 pounds of fine gold dust a year.

The largest dredge ever made was the 12,000-ton BIMA (named after the Asian god of good fortune), which was designed to extract tin from Indonesia in the 1970s with its 30-cubic-foot buckets. It was brought to Alaska in 1987 to remove gold from the floor of the Bering Sea. The machine, however, was shut down in 1990 because it was not profitable.

ECONOMICS OF HEAVY EQUIPMENT

The construction of heavy equipment is a multibillion-dollar, global industry. In the United States alone, the top 200 industrial owners of heavy equipment have more than $60 billion in equipment, with ten companies owning more than $1 billion worth of heavy machinery.

From horses to computerized machinery, the progression of harvesters illustrates how modernity has brought increasing productivity to farms. What a team of horses and a crew of workers could accomplish with a harvester in the course of several weeks, can now be done in a day by a single operator using a modern combine.

CENTER: *The studs and chisels of a continuous mining machine knock off blocks of coal and rock from the face of the mine. The machine is controlled by an attached box held by the operator.*

ABOVE: *Old meets new as a farmer on a burro greets the driver of a giant truck in Russia. The two symbols of the past and present met at the building site of the Toktogul hydropower station on the Naryn River in the former Kirghiz Soviet Socialist Republic in 1974.*

The farming magazine *Implement Trade Journal* published an article during World War I comparing the costs of operating a tractor versus the expenses of a single horse. At first glance the "iron hide" tractor didn't seem to fare so well. The total daily cost of owning and operating a 15- to 30-horsepower tractor was $11.80, six times greater than the daily $1.88 estimated cost of using a horse. But when the magazine looked at the costs in relation to output, the tractor proved to be a far more efficient way to farm. It cost 2.3 cents to haul a bushel of wheat 10 miles by tractors versus 7.5 cents by horse, 98 cents to plow an acre by tractor versus $2.33 by horse, and 27 cents to harvest an acre compared with 35 cents by horse. The magazine reeached this conclusion after analyzing the cost of buying a tractor, operating it, providing fuel, making repairs, the amount of labor involved, and the rate of production. "The figures show the advantage of a tractor over horse power."

Eighty years later horses are out of the farming business, but equipment operators are using the same kind of analysis to figure out the most cost-effective ways to complete projects. The reason that heavy equipment mushroomed as an industry in the twentieth century is because of economics. It is usually cheaper to have a handful of people operating a large piece of machinery than to have a small army of workers equipped with tools to perform the same task. As the demands for energy, buildings, tunnels, roads, felling trees, and other undertakings have reached massive proportions, the demand for heavy equipment has grown in step. In the United States alone, there were more than 200 companies with $60 billion or more worth of heavy equipment, according to *Construction Equipment* magazine, with ten companies owning heavy equipment worth $1 billion or more. It is a multibillion-dollar industry that arose out of a need, ironically enough, to find less expensive ways to build roads, dig mines, and undertake other huge earthmoving projects. Given· the scope of work involved in even medium-size projects, there is an enormous incentive to drive down the cost per yard of moving materials. And that is the bottom line.

In many cases, bigger machines mean greater efficiencies. The Komatsu D575A-2 Super Dozer is the biggest bulldozer in the world, almost double the size of the next largest dozer. It costs about $1.8 million to

buy, also about twice as much as the nearest competitor. But its operating costs are 50 to 55 percent greater while its rate of production is about 80 percent higher. When all of the math is done, Komatsu projected that its new machine would reduce costs per yard by 10 percent, an estimate that has been borne out by on-the-job performance. Similarly, giant draglines are models of efficiency for moving earth. Using giant buckets operated by a single person transporting hundreds of tons of earth with a single scoop is a much cheaper way to move mountains of earth than using a team of drivers working shovels and a fleet of giant trucks.

On the other hand, a giant dragline can cost $30 million or more to build, and not everyone needs a bulldozer to shove 100 cubic yards of dirt at a time. There is such a thing as overdoing it. Using a bigger machine doesn't do any good if you don't need such a big machine in the first place. The cost of the extra capacity ups the cost per yard. Even when the production costs are relatively low compared with those of other machines, they can still be steep, which is why most giant-scale mining machines operate on a 24-hour-a-day basis: it takes a lot of scoops of dirt to pay off a $30 million bill.

When figuring out what equipment to use for large projects, engineers work backward.

They look at the amount of material that needs to be moved, distances involved, types of materials, labor costs, and several other factors to come up with the optimum mix of machines. The number of variables and factors involved makes this a complicated task. Doubling the amount of material being moved doesn't automatically mean the number of machines used is doubled. A single change in the mix might mean that the entire fleet has to be altered. For big projects, big machines tend to be preferred because they are cheaper on a cost-per-yard basis. Economies of scale often make for greater efficiencies. But companies do not acquire big machines for the sake of their bigness. If 20 small machines will accomplish the same amount of work more cheaply than one big one, then the company will go with the smaller-machines option. Every situation is different.

Similarly, manufacturers of heavy equipment have to decide whether it is worth the investment into research, development, and new tool-making machinery to make bigger and bigger machines. Giant dump trucks got progressively bigger on a regular basis until the 1980s when they leveled off at 240 tons. At that point, tire companies balked at building tires that could carry loads that heavy. The amount of money involved was too high to justify the returns from the small demand they anticipated. By keeping the trucks at 240 tons, the size of shovels used to load the trucks was also capped. There was no reason to buy a bigger and more expensive shovel if it still took three passes with a shovel to fill it. When in 1996 a new 300-ton truck was built and successfully sold in the marketplace by Komatsu, other companies decided to follow Komatsu's lead and build bigger trucks. This may, in turn, unleash a new round of bigger shovels.

In general, engineers expect several types of machines such as draglines, mining shovels, and giant dump trucks to continue to get bigger. Most of the mines that were easy to get to have been exploited. Mining companies anticipate having to dig deeper and in more remote regions to continue to meet the enormous and growing energy demands of modern society. In addition, pressure to keep costs down are enormous in the race of an increasingly global economy. These two factors will continue to push companies to employ economies of scale to build even bigger machines to accomplish bigger jobs for less money.

Tunneling Machines

As in most earthmoving endeavors, ancient engineers found ways to tunnel through the earth without the aid of giant machines. Egyptian workers armed with copper chisels excavated labyrinths underneath the pyramids. Indian Buddhists carved out miles of spectacular tunnels as temples from 600 to 200 B.C. Persian engineers dug an incredible 170,000 miles of irrigation tunnels called *qanats* starting 2,500 years ago, which still provide a mainstay for Iranian farms. Instead of engines, rotating discs, and large drills to penetrate the earth, they used muscle and hand tools, a condition worldwide that did not change significantly until well into the Industrial Revolution when primitive mechanized drills and gunpowder were developed.

It wasn't until about 1850, however, that the first significant developments in modern tunnel machinery occurred. The new demand for railroad tunnels and the growing need for coal and minerals underground pushed the inventiveness of tunnel engineers. Around 1850 the first hard-rock tunneling machines were invented using steam power and compressed-air rock drilling machines. Rock drills invented to dig the 8-mile Mount Cenis tunnel between Italy and France, as well as the 4³/₄-mile Hoosac Tunnel in western Massachusetts, proved to be successful prototypes. Combined with the advent of nitroglycerine to replace gunpowder, the drill-and-blast method became the predominant tactic for digging tunnels, inhibiting the development of other excavating techniques.

Two major innovations, however, took bloom after World War II. One was the development of full-face tunnel boring machines (see next section), which were essentially giant drills, and the other was the invention and evolution of boom-type cutterheads, also known as *roadheaders* or *boomheaders*. Simple versions of these machines were used in Russian coal mines in the 1930s, and in 1949 Hungarian engineer Z. Ajtay invented what is considered the first modern boom-type cutter-loader machine. The cutterhead consisted of a series of rotating discs operated by chains fitted with picks. It was mounted at the end of a boom attached to a crawler. The cutterhead bored a hole into the coal face, and the material fell onto a conveyor belt that removed the debris without having to remove the machine, which was a major improvement. Rapid advances were made in the efficiency of the machine by placing an engine directly in the boom and improving the discs, and within a few years there were more than 1,000 cutterheads working Russian mines and tunnels. The innovation spread beyond the Eastern Bloc within a decade, and several companies were making the cutterheads for tunnels and mines.

Operated by a single person, the

In 1991 at the Selby coalfield in northern England two tunnels were excavated under the exact same conditions, one by boom-type cutterheads, the other by a full-face tunnel boring machine. The full-face tunnel boring machine's average weekly penetration was 330 feet, or twice the pace of the cutterheads. The cutterheads, however, were put into operation much more quickly and were less costly. Engineers concluded that for small-scale tasks, cutterheads were the better option, but full-face tunnel boring machines were more cost effective for tunnels longer than half a mile.

machines consist of a chassis mounted on crawler tracks holding a boom on the front. At the end of the boom is a cylinder- or pineapple-shaped cutterhead brimming with picks and/or disks. The head rotates, tearing away at the tunnel face. Typically, a cut is made at the bottom of the face and then a series of other cuts are made above it as the material falls onto a conveyor belt below. This is called *slewing.* The advantages of these boom machines is that they apply a great deal of force in a targeted area and that they allow ample room for other workers to erect steel arches and other supports for the tunnel. They are also more flexible in their applications. Boom cutterheads are being used in all sorts of innovative ways by mining companies to enhance their production. However, for tunneling purposes, full-face tunnel boring machines are faster and more efficient machines for medium- and soft-rock excavation in large-scale operations of a half mile or longer. In addition, the machines are often not as effective tunneling through hard rock, such as quartz, as the traditional drill-and-blast method.

ABOVE: *Until post-World War II, drills were the standard equipment used for excavating tunnels. This small drill is in the Wesfrob Mines at the Queen Charlotte Islands, off the coast of British Columbia, Canada.*

FACING PAGE: *A cutterhead grinds away in the Chunnel. First used in Russian coal mines, the machines were fully developed after World War II for digging tunnels. One of their chief advantages is that while the cylinder digs the hole from an extended boom, there is plenty of room beneath to remove the resulting debris.*

ABOVE: *A boom-type cutterhead sits astride the rear section of a full-face tunnel-boring machine used in the construction of the Chunnel. Although full-face tunnel-boring machines are extremely powerful, they are also expensive and only used for large projects. The much smaller, but still powerful, cutterheads are often more effective for small-scale projects.*

ABOVE: *A powerful drill at work in an underground tunnel. Drills are often used to dig holes for explosives.*

Full-face Tunnel Boring Machines

The first full-face tunnel boring machine was invented by J. D. Burton of England in 1870s with the purpose of digging a tunnel underneath the English Channel. Although the stone-cutting machine wasn't strong enough to perform the job, it used many of the same principles as today's monstrous mole-like machines. Seven feet in diameter, the cutterhead at the front was fastened to a massive iron frame braced against the sides of the tunnel. The cutterhead consisted of two face plates each carrying six steel disc cutters. Burton thus identified two of the fundamental aspects of today's machines: the use of disc cutters and the application of force that is not just powerful but is also from a massive machine that is stiff in a fixed position. His invention, however, suffered from other mechanical deficiencies. Although other similar and improved machines were built and actually started a tunnel under the English Channel, the machines were only effective in soft rock and were less efficient than more traditional drilling and blasting methods.

But in 1950 in the United States, James S. Robbins & Associates invented the Model 910-101 Tunnel Boring Machine, or the "Mittry mole," named after F. K. Mittry, who played a role in its invention. Twenty-six feet in diameter, the history-making machine was used to help dig a series of tunnels for the Oahe Dam project in South Dakota. The borer consisted of two counter-rotating heads—an inner head with three cutting arms fitted with discs, and an outer head bristling with six cutting arms that rotated in a direction opposite that of the inner disc. Two 200-horsepower motors powered the heads, and a 25-horsepower engine moved the entire 90-foot-long unit back and forth on a track. The machine, which had now benefited from the tremendous advances in mechanical engineering since the nineteenth century, easily cut through the Pierre shale, advancing at a world-firecord pace of 161 feet in a single day. The company soon manufac-

▲ A rotary cutting head will typically consist of three to eight radial arms fitted with discs and chisels. Spinning at a rate of between three and eight cycles per minute, they can be anywhere from 6 to 36 feet in diameter. Because of the capital expense in building the machines, they typically are used for projects that are a mile or longer.

▲ The development of full-face tunnel boring machines came out of the coal industry. James S. Robbins, the inventor of the first successful full-face tunnel boring machine, had been an engineer for coal mining companies when he was hired to develop a tunnel-boring machine for the construction of the Oahe Dam in South Dakota.

TOP: *Workers look on as a full-face tunnel boring machine cuts its way through the chalk underground beneath the English Channel.*

ABOVE: *A 27-foot-diameter Robbins full-face tunnel-boring machine on the factory floor. The back side of the machine consists of a complex arrangement of equipment that both provides power to drive the machine and removes the churned-up earth to the rear for removal from the tunnel.*

tured more of the machines (including one 37 feet), and several other companies followed suit, bringing new advances and improvements to the new technology.

Full-face tunnel boring machines are basically giant, self-contained drills. The cutter in the front usually rotates at a speed of between three and eight rotations per minute. As the cutter spins, reinforced steel discs and chisels sheer away rock, stone, and earth, which fall through an opening and into the machine and onto a conveyor belt that removes the material for disposal. The force for the cutting edge is provided by hydraulic rams that secure themselves against the lining of the tunnel. The amount of force being applied by modern machines can be 10 million pounds or more. How fast the machine rotates, the types of picks and discs used to cut the rock, the

dimensions of the machine, and a host of other factors all determine how the custom-built machines are designed. When digging in wet conditions, the machines can be hermetically sealed to keep water out, with debris being forced out the rear with an Archimedes' screw. Between the cutter mechanism, conveyor belts, pumps, tunnel lining components, and other aspects of the machines, they can be as long as 1,000 feet.

Because of their cost and the extended amount of time it takes to build and set them up, they are usually only cost-effective for large-scale projects. They are especially suited for digging through soft rock areas. Hardened metal buttons and tungsten carbide picks and cutters are used for hard-rock digging, but in spite of their size and power the machines are often not powerful enough to penetrate harder rock.

ABOVE: *As the full-face tunnel-boring machine digs its giant whole, teams of workers place cement segment rings along the face of the resulting tunnel. The rings both support the tunnel and provide leverage for the machine to apply its force forward.*

LEFT: *A 35-foot diameter Robbins full-face tunnel-boring machine. Each machine is custom-made for the particular tunnel it will excavate. The design of its face and the types of drills and chisels used depend on the conditions that it will work in. This machine has yet to be armed with its digging utensils.*

Fifteen thousand workers took part in digging the Channel Tunnel. They removed 283 million cubic feet of chalky material, making it the largest tunnel ever built. The $15 billion project is the most expensive privately financed construction project ever undertaken.

ABOVE: *One of 11 full-face tunnel-boring machines used in the construction of the Channel Tunnel sits at rest in the giant tunnel. The machines were up 26 feet in diameter and had eight arms studded with cutting picks and discs to cut through the chalk and dirt. The machines were hundreds of*

ABOVE, INSET: *The British side of the Channel Tunnel commences at Shakespeare Cliffs in Kent. The project, which consists of two train tunnels and an auxiliary tunnel, has 100 miles of railroad tracks, 20,000 lighting fixtures, 1,200 telephones, 600 special doors, and massive infrastructure sys-*

TUNNEL

Discussed for more than two centuries, sporadically pursued for 150 years, and actually built in 99 months, the construction of the Channel Tunnel, completed in 1994, is the largest ever privately financed construction project and the biggest tunnel in the world.

The idea of crossing the English Channel in means other than a boat was first broached in 1751 by the Amiens Academy in France, but the first realistic proposal was made in the 1830s by French engineer Aimé Thomé de Gamond. He conducted geological and hydrographical surveys and made the happy the discovery that most of the ground under the Channel consists of chalk, a relatively easy surface to bore through.

After decades of perserverence, the United Kingdom and France agreed to build the tunnel. In 1881, tunneling commenced. Although modern engineers believe today that tunnelers had the wherewithal to complete the project, the British pulled the plug. Concerned about the tunnel's serving as a military route for Continental invaders, British leaders nixed the project.

But in the 1970s, interest was revived once again. In 1986, France and the United Kingdom signed an agreement to build the tunnel together. After an immense amount of haggling and negotiation between the governments and potential contractors, a consortium of five British and five French companies called Transmanche-Link (TML) was selected to build the tunnel, and the concession to own and operate it for 55 years (10 more years were later added) was awarded to Eurotunnel, an Anglo-French company.

Construction crews started in 1987 to build the 31-mile tunnel connecting Cheriton, near Folkestone in England, to the French town of Sangatte just west of Calais. Swirled in controversy much of the time, construction went forward close to schedule nevertheless. In 1994, Queen Elizabeth II of the United Kingdom and French President Mitterand officially opened the tunnel for commercial and passenger rail travel.

The Channel Tunnel today consists of three parallel 31-mile tunnels: two main tunnels 25 feet in diameter used for high-speed single- and double-story trains, and a smaller 16-foot-wide service tunnel in between. All three tunnels are connected by cross passages every 1,200 feet. The average depth of the tunnel is 148 feet.

Building the Channel Tunnel was an immense project involving thousands of workers, and more than 100 miles of railroad track.

Eleven tunnel-boring machines (TBMs) were used for the project, with different machines employed for different conditions depending on the wetness of the soil and chalk. The cutterheads on the TBMs were as wide as 26 feet. Armed with cutting picks or discs, the eight-armed cutterheads turned at a rate of 3.3 rotations per minute with a thrust of up to 4,220 tons.

As the cutterheads churned through the ground, the chalk and earth fell onto conveyor belts that carried the dirt back through the tunnel to wagons that hauled it out of the passageway. In wet areas watertight bulkheads sealed the machine closed, similar to a submarine. The *spoil*, the excavated rock and earth, was carried out by an Archimedes' screw. These gigantic mechanical moles contained as many as 700 motors and mechanisms and were typically about 600 feet long, including the conveyor belt and hydraulic power system.

Construction crews installed concrete segment rings as the machine moved forward. Each ring was about 5 feet wide and consisted of between five and eight segments. The lining provided the foundation that the TBMs' grippers held on to. Tunneling started in February 1988 and ended in June 1991.

Having completed the excavation, TML installed railroad tracks, 20,000 lighting fixtures, 1,200 telephones, 600 special doors, the railroad tracks, and massive ventialation, cooling, drainage, and fire protection systems. When it was over, the bill came to $15 billion, or about double the original estimate.

ABOVE: *An English worker drills his way to France. Fifteen thousand workers took part in the digging of the Channel Tunnel, also known as the Eurotunnel or Chunnel.*

LEFT: *The Channel Tunnel was built with machines and workers digging the tunnel from both sides of the English Channel. A very happy British worker celebrates as a full-face tunnel-boring machine completes its mission and meets up with the French side of the tunnel.*

RIGHT: *The cavernous inside of the Channel Tunnel. The largest privately financed construction project in the history of the world, the massive tunnel took 8 years to complete, cost more than $15 billion, and involved the removal of 283 million cubic feet of chalky clay and dirt.*

ABOVE: *An offshore oil rig is a behemoth of a machine. Standing high above the ocean floor on massive jacks and/or cement pillars, they house scores of workers and pump thousands of barrels of oil a day. This one is equipped with five giant cranes for hoisting and hauling purposes.*

ABOVE, INSET: *An oil rig on the North Sea has drills that go as much 1,000 feet under the water before touching the ocean floor.*

LEFT: *A giant offshore oil rig platform is hauled from San Francisco Harbor out to sea off the California coast.*

OIL RIGS

Ever since Edwin L. Drake drilled the first successful oil well in 1859 with a 6-horsepower steam engine in western Pennsylvania, the petroleum industry has been building bigger and increasingly sophisticated oil rigs with deeper drills to reach farther into the center of the earth. From wildcat oil companies in Texas to major wells in the Middle East to smaller mobile rigs developed in the early part of the twentieth century, the prospect of tapping "black gold" underground has driven the growth and development of oil-excavating equipment. Far and away the most impressive of these stationary machines are the offshore oil rigs, some as tall as skyscrapers, firmly planted to the seafloor, which brave the giant waves and fierce weather of the ocean.

By the 1850s, oil had found a new purpose. The increasing industrialization of western Europe and the United States created a demand for oil as a lubricant in machinery. When Drake was hired by the Seneca Oil Company to oversee an oil well, oil was selling for two dollars a gallon. Although there were isolated spots where oil could be found in streams and bubbling to the surface of the ground, nobody had developed a way to plumb oil from under the earth. Using modified equipment that had been utilized to drill salt wells, Drake (who had previously been a train conductor) built his well in Titusville, Pennsylvania, in the spring of 1859. Groundwater persistently flooded the well. He solved the problem by inserting sections of cast-iron pipe 32 feet into the ground with the drill being placed inside the pipe for further excavation. At 69 feet, Drake and his men discovered oil. The first oil well yielded an estimated 10 to 20 barrels a day, doubling the national production of oil. The discovery set off an oil boom that has never really stopped as even more productive and important uses for oil were discovered.

While Drake's setup was so flimsy that it burned to the ground two months after the discovery and his enterprise later went bankrupt, the sophistication, scope, and scale of oil-drilling equipment has gone through several generations of dramatic improvement. Some wells are as much as 5 miles deep. Most oil wells are done by a rotary method in which an engine powers a rotary turntable that holds a collection of pipes with a drill bit at the other end. The rotation turns the drill bit into the ground, bringing the pipes deeper and deeper.

The most daunting of all oil wells are offshore rigs, which use the same method but need to have a steady platform to remain still despite the motions of the ocean. In shallow water close to shore a pier is often built from which to drill. Fixed, stand-alone platforms that are set by pilings into the seafloor can be built up to depths of about 100 feet. One method for building oil rigs for deeper depths is a jack-up platform. A self-contained oil drilling rig is built on a floating base that is towed to the desired location. Massives jacks that are attached below the base are then lowered until they reach the ocean floor.

The largest oil-drilling rigs, such as the Gullfaks C in the North Sea, which is 1,148 feet tall, use giant concrete pillars that are built in an elaborate process in the water. First caissons, which are hollow concrete supports, are built in dry dock. They will form the base of the rig. The dock is flooded and a tugboat tows the caissons to a sheltered site where the supports are flooded and submerged under the water. Concrete pillars are built on top of the caissons, and then the platform is constructed on top of the pillars. Water is then partially pumped out of the caissons, thus buoying the giant machine high above sea level. A tugboat pulls the monstrous rig to its location where it sinks gently down to the ocean floor as water refills the caissons once again. In the case of the Gullfaks C, the rig was towed 108 miles off the coast of Norway to extract oil from wells that had already been dug. The platform, which is perched 98 feet above sea level, has a helipad, giant drilling derrick, several cranes, and facilities to house the rig's crew of 330 people.

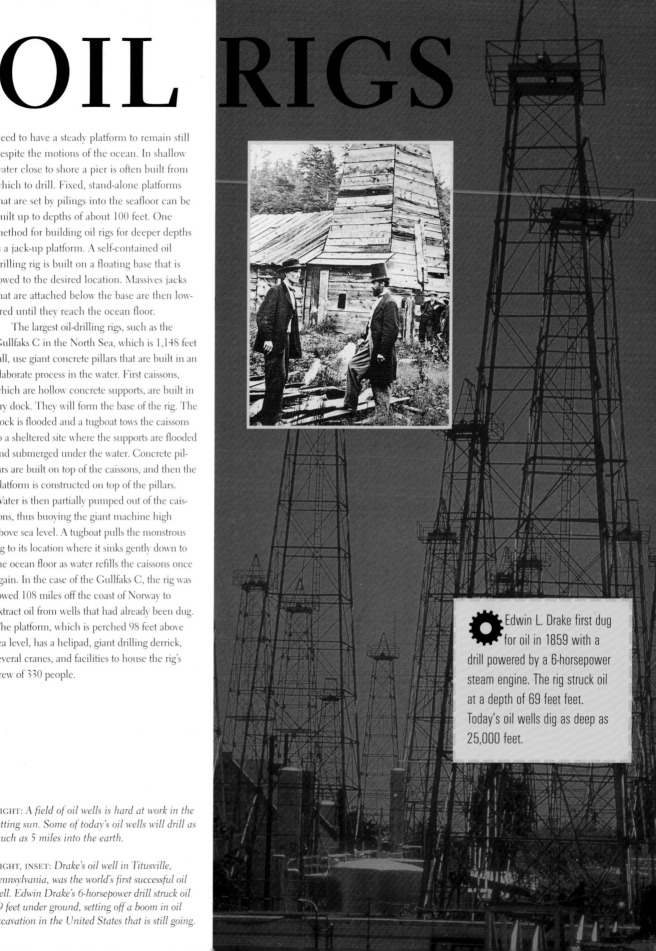

RIGHT: *A field of oil wells is hard at work in the setting sun. Some of today's oil wells will drill as much as 5 miles into the earth.*

RIGHT, INSET: *Drake's oil well in Titusville, Pennsylvania, was the world's first successful oil well. Edwin Drake's 6-horsepower drill struck oil 69 feet under ground, setting off a boom in oil excavation in the United States that is still going.*

Edwin L. Drake first dug for oil in 1859 with a drill powered by a 6-horsepower steam engine. The rig struck oil at a depth of 69 feet feet. Today's oil wells dig as deep as 25,000 feet.

AMPHIBIOUS

The Komatsu Amphibious Bulldozer looks like a cross between a large bulldozer and a peculiar-looking yacht. It has proven to be more popular in Japan than the United States where it has barely been used.

The Japanese heavy-equipment manufacturer Komatsu has taken its bulldozers underwater. The D155W Amphibious Bulldozer is a one-of-a-kind piece of equipment designed for moving rocks, sand, and dirt in water up to 23 feet deep. Rarely seen in the United States, it has mainly been used in Japan for a wide range of purposes having to do with coastal and river construction work. It is used as an alternative or complement to dredging equipment.

The amphibious bulldozer can be operated by either direct wire control or remote radio control from a control box operated on land. Controls, which can be carried by an operator, are arranged in a way similar to those of ordinary bulldozers. The radio control range is 160 feet.

The machine is operated by a 270-horsepower engine much like the one used in standard Komatsu bulldozers, although several modifications have been made. The engine and radiators are held in a box structure that can be hermetically sealed when in the water. All power-line components—transmission, torque convertor, steering system, and final drive—are enclosed in watertight structures. Exterior bolts, nuts, and washers are treated for corrosion. Bearings are made of Teflon to avoid the need for lubrication. A special type of paint is coated on the vehicle to resist seawater corrosion. There are two radiator systems. A fan-cooling system is used when the machine operates on land. An environmental water-cooling radiator is engaged for water use.

Able to work both underwater and on land, the most striking feature of the bulldozer at first glance is a periscope-like tower sticking off the top of where an operator might normally sit. The 15-foot mast, however, is no periscope. The mast is part of the intake and exhaust system for the engine. The top of the mast has a series of lights and horns that are triggered by mechanical problems such as the oil pressure, or engine water temperature being too high, the pump exceeding its capacity, and the vehicle operating at an incline of 21 degrees or more.

Like normal bulldozers, the machine is equipped with a hydraulic ripper and dozer

BULLDOZER

blade. The blade is 12½ feet wide. It has a capacity of 5 cubic yards with a front apron and side plates attached. The bulldozer is 30 feet long and 13 feet wide. It can travel up to 4 miles per hour going forward and 4.8 miles per hour in reverse. Its operating weight on land is 95,000 pounds and in water 61,000 pounds. The amphibious bulldozer's digging capacity is 30 cubic yards per hour.

Komatsu states that the machine offers several advantages over dredges, including its digging capacity, maneuverability, relative ease to level the water floor, and ability to move earth without having to build a temporary dam with sheet piles. Some of the projects that the amphibious bulldozer has been used for include leveling a river bottom, dredging a berth for fishing vessels, digging foundations for breakwaters, excavating and refilling harbors, dredging fairways, expanding fishing port facilities, and deepening anchorage ground.

▲ In a typical project, the Komatsu amphibious bulldozer excavates and removes 2,620 cubic yards of sandy soil from the seafloor 16 feet below water in two weeks. High waves limit the use of a dredge for the project.

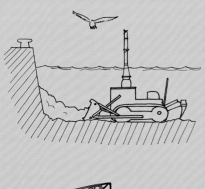

LEFT: *The amphibious bulldozer can work in water up to 23 feet deep and is operated by remote control from land.*

BELOW, LEFT: *Dredging a berth for fishing vessels is a typical task for an amphibious bulldozer. Using its ripper to dig into the rock and hard clay bottom and its apron to haul the fill, the bulldozer worked in water up to 5 feet deep to remove close to 40,000 cubic yards. The job took 4 months.*

TOP: *The apron of the Komatsu Amphibious Bulldozer unloads its soggy haul near the waterfront.*

ABOVE: *The mast of the Komatsu Amphibious Bulldozer is equipped with electronic equipment to control the operation of the machine, as well as horns and lights that are triggered if anything goes wrong with the machine underwater.*

FARMING & FORESTRY

Some of the first uses of modern heavy equipment were applied to farming and forestry. The first crawlers—so common on excavators, bulldozers, and other heavy equipment today—were invented at the dawn of the twentieth century for hauling logs through the icy woods of the northern United States and Canada. Many types of modern heavy equipment are derived from tractors. The first bulldozers were tractors with heavy blades placed in front; the first graders were tractors with blades fitted underneath the driver's seat; and the first scrapers were tractors with large bowls fitted to the rear.

Modern farming and forestry equipment is specialized equipment, designed to prepare, plant, cultivate, and harvest the greatest produce by expending the least amount of energy and causing a minimal amount of damage. These machines, while not as spectacular in size as mining equipment, are marvels of efficiency, capable of performing multiple tasks that it once took teams of people to accomplish. Farming and forestry machines have released millions upon millions of people from the toil of working the land, and that by itself is an impressive legacy.

A John Deere tractor cultivates a soybean field.

TRACTORS

Tractors are not as impressive in scale as other categories of equipment such as those used for strip-mining, but the development of agricultural machinery has arguably transformed the lives and lifestyles of more people in the industrialized world than any other type of equipment.

Agricultural machinery literally plowed the way for industrialization. More than 90 percent of the people in the United States in the early nineteenth century lived on farms. This was not because the masses had an affection for working outdoors, but rather because of the primitive state of farming technology.

Farming was drudgery. Limited by the speed of oxen and the endurance of their own bodies, farmers struggled to cultivate fields largely with hand tools and only the most primitive technologies. It took two men working with a team of oxen a full day to plow a single acre. Once grown, the crops were cut, threshed, and processed by hand. Farmers struggled simply to grow enough for their own families, much less food for city folk.

Two hundreds years later the situation is radically different. Today 2 percent of the United States' workforce are farmers. They not only generate enough food and fiber to feed 260 million of their fellow residents, but also export significant amounts of crop. Technology, largely in the form of agricultural machinery, allowed this reversal of fortune to occur. And of all the developments in agriculture, perhaps none was as significant as the invention of the tractor at the turn of the twentieth century.

No longer constrained by the limits of human and beastly stamina, tractors could pull plows and other attachments faster, longer, cheaper, and more reliably than any combination of people and horses. What once took a full day to plow three acres with a team of horses, took two hours with a primitive tractor in 1930. Today, a tractor with a 12-bottom plow trailing behind plows as much as 10 acres an hour. Moreover, improvements made in the twentieth century allowed the tractor to serve as a mobile source of power.

Modern tractors descended from steam crawlers developed in the nineteenth century.

ABOVE: Harvest time throughout the nineteenth century was a back-breaking, labor-intensive task. Technological improvements in harvesting had been few and far between until the 1800s.

RIGHT: An Avery 12-horsepower tractor was one of the hundreds of tractors that came into the farming scene at the beginning of the twentieth century to help mechanize agriculture.

BELOW: Horsepower really came from horses prior to the advent of tractors. A woman guides two horses that pull a reaper and binder in a field of barley.

LEFT: *Two large steam tractors reap a field of wheat in the western United States. Because of the size of the early tractors, manufacturers had to build giant wheels to displace the weight as broadly as possible, otherwise the tractors sank into the ground. One of the problems with such wide wheels, however, was that it compressed huge swaths of land.*

BELOW: *Harvesting time in Indiana in 1935. The 1930s saw the advent of pneumatic rubber tires, hydraulic lifts, and diesel engines, all of which contributed to making the tractor an essential piece of equipment on any farm.*

Heavy, cumbersome, and unreliable, steam crawlers had limited applications on farms and did not flourish. But with the invention of the combustible engine, new possibilities arose. By the beginning of the twentieth century several different types of tractors, mostly on crawlers, were being manufactured in the United States and Europe.

The outbreak of World War I accelerated the development of the tractor. Horses were being killed at a rate of up to 1 million a month on the front lines, young men were removed from farms and sent to the front, and there was a tremendous need to increase agricultural productivity. Tractors proved to be a salvation both on the home front, where farming productivity rose 50 percent or more between 1916 and 1918, and in the war zones where the machines proved to be reliable haulers of men and materiel.

Having both proven their worth and been exposed to millions of operators, tractors soared in popularity after the war. In the United States, Henry Ford manufactured the enormously popular and inexpensive Fordson tractor, making it accessible to the general population, and at one time dominating tractor sales with 75 percent of the market. Innovations such as pneumatic rubber tires, the hydraulic lift, and diesel engines improved the efficiency of the tractor, making it an essential piece of equipment on most farms in the industrialized world.

Further improvements were made after World War II when tractor sales once again soared on a global scale. Increasingly sophisticated applications of technology and advances in the capacity of tractors allowed farmers to do more with fewer people than ever before.

▲ Tractors were the inspiration for a wide variety of other machines including military tanks, bulldozers, and graders. The inventor of the tank, British Lieutenant Colonel Ernest Swinton, described the Holt Caterpillar tractor plant as "the cradle of the tank."

LEFT, CENTER: *Manufacturers appealed to farmers' "common sense" as they persuaded them to see the financial and practical advantages of mechanized tractors over horses. Field demonstrations at local fairs were a popular way for manufacturers to show off their machines at work.*

LEFT: *A crawler tractor plows a field. In the nineteenth century a farmer working with a team of horses would plow about 3 acres a day. By 1930, a tractor could accomplish the same task in about 2 hours. Today, a tractor with a 12-bottom plow is capable of plowing 3 acres in about 18 minutes.*

Giant Tractors

LEFT: *John Deere 9400 is the largest tractor made by Deere & Company. It weighs 16 tons, has a 425-horsepower, 6-cylinder engine, and carries a 270-gallon fuel tank.*

Since 1960, the number of farms in North America has dropped in half to slightly more than 2 million. At the same time, the size of the average farm has soared from 302 acres in the United States in 1960 to 470 acres today. In Canada, the average size of a farm in 1996 was 624 acres.

Bigger farms have required bigger tractors to work the land with fewer farmers. A far cry from the horse teams of the 1800s or the primitive tractors built at the start of the twentieth century, today's four-wheel-drive tractors have the power of hundreds of horses, performing tasks in a fraction of the time.

The power derived from a 400-horsepower tractor is enough to pull and drive the largest attachments needed to plow, fertilize, seed, cultivate, spray, and harvest farms with hundreds, if not thousands, of acres. Because farms outside of North America tend to be smaller (the average farm in western Europe is 40 acres), most of the giant-tractor market is in North America.

In 1996, more than 120,000 tractors were sold in the United States, of which 22,000 were two-wheel-drive tractors with over 100 horsepower and 4,600 were four-wheel-drive tractors. The number of four-wheel-drive tractors sold is more than double that of 10 years earlier.

As far as equipment costs are concerned, the economics favors larger farms with larger tractors. According Deere & Company, the operating costs of a 300-horsepower tractor on a farm are less than those of a 150-horsepower tractor tending a farm for almost all aspects of farming. In some cases, such as plowing, the difference is as much as 25 percent.

Manufacturers of the giant tractors include Deere & Company, New Holland, Caterpillar, Agco, Case Corporation, and Belarus, a Russian company. The largest tractor ever made was a 1,000-horsepower machine by Komatsu in the early 1980s, but most of the

Depending on a wide number of factors, the cost of a new 400-plus-horsepower tractor is typically between $150,000 and $200,000.

ABOVE: *A John Deere tractor plows through a field in Flathead Valley, Montana. A tractor like this can plow 100 acres a day.*

commercial giant tractors today are in the 200- to 400-plus-horsepower range.

The distinguishing characteristic of these machines is, not surprisingly, their size and power. Case's largest tractor, a 425-horsepower Steiger 9390, for example, weighs 16 tons, is 12 feet high, carries a 270-gallon fuel tank, and can be carried by as many as twelve 6-foot-high tires. The biggest tractors are articulated and have as many as three tires on a side to disperse the impact of the tractor's heavy weight on the soil. Operators drive the tires in between the rows of crops to prevent damage. Floodlights, electrical terminals, and infrared lights are also typical features of a giant tractor.

Farmers from yesteryear wouldn't just gape at the enormous size of today's tractors. Huge advances have been made in safety, comfort and computerization. Deere & Company's 9000 Series tractors have large cabs for the operator to sit in nylon-webbed retractable seats, complete with adjustable armrests, heating and air-conditioning units, and a space specifically designed to hold a laptop computer. The computerized control panel consists of an array of switches, knobs, and digitial numbers that operate the tractor and reveal information ranging from the number of acres covered to the percentage of wheel slip.

ABOVE AND LEFT: *The New Holland 9882 tractor is 12 feet high, 10 feet wide and 22 feet long. Its operating weight is 40,000 pounds, and the tractor carries a 425-horsepower Cummins N14-425 in-line 6-cylinder engine. It has two fuel tanks that hold 230 gallons. Depending on the needs of the operator, this tractor can have as many as 12 tires.*

Below: A giant New Holland 9482 tractor and a New Holland combine harvester can accomplish quite a bit working together during harvesttime.

ABOVE: *Twelve tires are used for this giant AGCO tractor, thus dispersing the weight of the tractor over 12 points of contact and reducing the ground pressure that can harm the growing capacity of the soil below. To avoid damaging produce, the driver must maneuver the wheels in between row crops.*

TRACTOR ATTACHMENTS

A tractor by itself offers little value to a farmer other than its transportation uses. The real value of a tractor on a farm is its capacity to pull and power a wide range of implements to work the land. There are three general categories of attachments: those that (1) prepare the field for crops, (2) treat the crops while growing, and (3) harvest the crops. A brief summary of some types of attachments commonly used and their purposes follows.

A Caterpillar Diesel 50 pulls a 60-foot harrow through a desolate section of Sacramento, California.

Assisted by three young boys that keep three 3-gang disc plows on course, a farmer drives an Avery tractor to plow a field for planting.

Drills

Drills allow farmers to plant seeds in a precise, fast, and efficient manner. There are two basic types of grain drills. One is a mechanically fed mechanism that forces seeds into the ground with a studded wheel that inserts the seed. Pneumatic drills, a more recent type of drill, rely on air power to distribute the seeds. The seeds are inserted through either a disc or slim hoe that cuts a hole in the ground. The grain is then covered with earth by means of harrows or other discs that are either attached to the drill or a trailing tractor. Some drills are designed to also fertilize at the same time.

Plows

Plows have been used by farmers for centuries as their primary cultivating tool. The purpose of a plow is to cut and turn slices of the earth to prepare for seeding. The type of plow used depends on a wide variety of factors including the depth of the cut, the type of crop to be planted, soil conditions, weather, and the desired finish. The working end of a plow is called the *moldboard*, a specially designed piece of metal that cuts through the earth. There are three main types of plows. Conventional plows have right-handed moldboards that cut the earth into furrows. Reversible plows, which are larger and more expensive, have left- and right-handed moldboards that leave a level field. Disc plows use rotating discs instead of moldboards to cut the earth and are more common in hot-weather regions. This extra disruption of the soil by moldboards allows the heat to dry out the soil.

Caterpillar D4 tractor pulls an offset disc harrow preparing seedbed for cotton on a 3,000-acre ranch in northwest Texas in 1956.

Cultivators

Cultivators do not so much turn the earth over as plows do, but rather break up compacted soil, allowing the free passage of air and water. The typical working depth of cultivating machinery is less than a moldboard plow. In some cases, cultivating is a viable alternative to plowing. Enhanced shattering of the soil can be achieved by cultivators with vibrating mechanisms. There are many different types of cultivators including chisel plows (slimmer versions of moldboard plows), rotary cultivators (powered blades that cut up the ground), and disc harrows (saucer-shaped discs that cut into the ground as they are moved by the tractor). Within each of these and other categories there are an extraordinarily diverse number of designs that are geared toward different crops and soil conditions.

Haymaking Machines

Turning grass into bales of hay is a three-step process. First, mowers cut the grass or other forage crop. There are several different types of mowers. They include rotary, drum, flail, and cutter bar mowers. The second step is conditioning the hay. Freshly cut grass has a moisture content of about 75 percent. That has to be lowered to 20 percent for safe storage, so the moisture content has to be reduced as quickly as possible through hay treatment: that expedites evaporation from the heat of the sun and the wind's breeze. Thus, when hay mowers cut the grass, they also have mechanism to bruise the stems, which in turn releases the saps. The bruises can be inflicted by pressing the hay against a drum or other hay, swinging nylon sticks from a rotary, pressing the hay between rollers, passing the hay through a horizontal rotor, or other methods. In order to speed the drying process, once cut, the hay can be redispersed with either rakes or *tedders* (rotating drum with rows of metal fingers) that spread the crop evenly.

New Jersey farmers gather and bale hay with a New Holland baler.

At present it costs $1.5 million or more for a farmer to fully equip a large farm of 1,000 acres or more with new equipment for plowing, planting, tending, and harvesting crops.

A haying machine cuts and sorts hay. The cut material is left on the ground where it will dry and be ready for baling.

Balers

The third and final step in making hay is collecting the cut, dried grass, picking it up, and pressing it into bales. Pickup or square balers typically collect up to about 80 pounds of hay, compress it into a rectangular shape, cut the sides, tie it, and eject the mass of materials as a bale of hay about 3 feet long and 1½ feet high. Some square balers, however, make bales of hay close to 3 feet high and 8 feet long. Round balers pick up the hay with rotating metal fins, process the material through a circular conveyor belt system until it reaches a certain size, and then eject the mass of materials out the rear of the baler. Some balers wrap the hay in twine. The biggest balers make round bales as big as 6 feet in diameter and weighing more than a ton.

Sprayers

Ground crop sprayers apply chemicals with diluted water to the soil or to growing crops for the control of disease, insects, and weeds. They are also employed to apply liquid fertilizers. Spray bars can be as wide as 75 feet and are either self-propelled, trailed, or mounted. There are a wide variety of sprayers with different types of nozzles, chemical mixing processes, and other features.

This tractor pulls a large cultivator across a field. Similar to a plow, the cultivator breaks up the compacted soil, allowing free passage of air and water. Cultivating can be an alternative to plowing.

Fertilizing Machines

Manure and fertilizer spreaders are relatively straightforward distribution machines attached to the rear of tractors. Manure spreaders are essentially trailers with a moving floor conveyor combined with a shredding and spreading mechanism that disperses manure onto the ground. The distribution of the manure is done on the side or rear of the trailer. Fertilizing distributors have similar mechanisms that will distribute the fertilizer with either a single rotary blaster or a series of smaller distribution points spread across a wide boom.

John Deere tractor plows a field in England.

A combine harvester does what its name implies. It combines all the elements of harvesting a crop—cutting, threshing and sorting—into a single machine. The harvester chews up the crop and spits it out as grain, straw, and chaff. It is an extraordinary machine, saving thousands of hours for farmers in what was once one of the most labor-intensive aspects of farming.

Although primitive horse-drawn combines were in the market through the first half of the twentieth century, it wasn't until 1938 that an Australian engineer, Tom Carrol, developed the first self-propelled machine. In 1944, the combine harvester made an enormous impression on the world of farming when 500 Massey-Harris machines were turned into the "harvest brigade." The small army of machines started

Combine Harvesters

to harvest in May in Texas and California and worked their way north, harvesting thousands of acres along the way.

In the 1960s and 1970s, engineers at International Harvester and New Holland developed a new combine harvester with axial threshing that greatly expanded the capacity of the machines. Rather than shaking the crop before threshing it, the new machines used friction and centrifugal force. This allowed for the construction of more compact machines that could harvest more crops faster. Combine harvesters are used on a wide range of crops, including cereals, grass, peas, beans, and corn. Virtually all aspects of the combine can be adjusted to suit the type of crop being harvested.

At the front of a combine harvester, a reciprocating knife cutter bar downs the crop at a rate of 1,000 cuts per minute. The felled stalks are forced into the central feeder house by an auger. The central feeder, which is typically one-third the length of the combine's cutting swath, carries the crop into the harvester on an elevating lift. The crop is fed into a threshing mechanism that consists of a rotating cylinder and a concave set of bars pressed close to the threshing cylinder. Spaces between the bars allow the threshed grain to fall into a tray below as the cylinder

rubs the ears of the crop. Depending on the crop, the speed of the spinning cylinder will vary from between 30 and 60 miles per hour. Between 75 and 90 percent of the grain is typically sorted in this phase.

The remaining crop is separated from the straw through different separating mechanisms. Straw walkers carry the crop to the back of the machine, vigorously shaking it with a rising and falling action. Again, as the heavier grain shakes loose it falls through to a tray below. Another type of separating mechanism employs a series of similar cylinder and concave combinations. When this process is completed, the chaff and straw are forced out the rear of the harvester.

The grain and chaff on the grain pan below are sorted with a pair of shaking sieves and a powerful fan. The shaking action of the sieves separates the grain while the fan keeps the sieves from being blocked. The top sieve allows everything through except long straws and partly threshed heads. The bottom sieve receives the materal and sorts it one last time, with a return auger carrying the material back to be rethreshed and another auger that pushes the good grain into a hopper to be stored.

ABOVE: *Teams of combine harvesters will often work together following the harvesting season in the midwestern and western United States. These three red combines are harvesting wheat. A single modern wheat combine can harvest 100 acres in a day.*

ABOVE, INSET: *A Caterpillar diesel tractor is teamed with two John Deere combines to harvest wheat in the state of Washington shortly after World War II. Working together, the team could cut 125 acres in 11 hours.*

BELOW: *Combine harvesters come in many different shapes and sizes for many different crops. This is a John Deere cotton harvester at work.*

ABOVE: *Two John Deere combine harvesters at work in a ripe barley field.*

RIGHT, INSET: *An early corn harvester at work with a nearby truck.*

RIGHT: *A modern corn combine harvester accomplishes the same task and more, faster, and more efficiently, and leaves a much tidier field in its wake.*

▲ The largest harvesters are typically run by engines with 200 or more horsepower, are 13 feet high and 30 feet long with a cutter bar as long as 30 feet, and can hold as much as 240 bushels of grain.

▲ Between 8,000 and 10,000 combine harvesters are usually sold a year in the United States. The largest manufacturers are Case, Deere & Company, and New Holland.

▲ A large combine harvester processes between 5 and 6 acres of corn an hour. Wheat combines do 100 acres in a day.

D eere & Company, founded in 1837 as a one-man blacksmith shop, is the world's largest manufacturer of agricultural equipment. Manufacturing the most tractors and combine harvesters sold in the United States, 15 percent in Europe, and a rapidly growing share in the rest of the globe, Deere & Company dominates the world of agricultural equipment. Sales in 1996 alone exceeded $6 billion. Indeed, the John Deere tractor has become an icon for the American farmer.

John Deere was a 33-year-old blacksmith when he moved in 1836 from Vermont to Illinois seeking opportunity. Like thousands of other settlers, he discovered that plows used in the Eastern and inland coastal states were virtually useless in the western prairie's heavier soil. The dirt quickly stuck to the wooden and iron moldboards of the plows. Using a discarded mill saw blade, Deere fashioned a new type of steel plow designed and shaped to cut through the soil with ease, without the soil's sticking to the moldboard.

The innovation proved to be the first commercially successful plow in the Midwest. Demand for Deere's plow soared. In 1847, Deere set up a manufacturing center in Moline, Illinois, on the Mississippi River. By 1850, Deere was producing 1,600 plows a year. The company and its plows played a major role in the opening up of the West through the rest of the century.

Two sets of major acquisitions in the early part of the twentieth century established Deere & Company as a major manufacturer of agricultural equipment. In 1911, the company bought six implement companies, including Van Brunt Manufacturing Company (the world's leading grain drill factory), Deere & Mansur Works (the world's largest manufactur-

er of corn planters), and Dain (a large manufacturer of hay stackers).

Deere & Company entered the tractor business in 1918 when it acquired Waterloo Gasoline Traction Company. Waterloo had been founded by John Froelich, who in 1892 built the first gasoline tractor that could travel both forward and backward. Deere & Company instantly became a major player in the tractor industry and quickly built upon that foundation. The company introduced its Model D in 1924, stressing its simplicity, and then in 1928 the GP with four power outlets: drawbar, belt pulley, power take-off, and power lift.

A lengthy list of innovations and improvements both with tractors and other types of farming machinery pushed the company to the forefront of its industry, and in 1963 Deere & Company became the world's largest manufacturer of agricultural machinery, a position it still holds today.

The breadth of Deere & Company products is extraordinary, ranging from 260-horsepower combines to compact backyard tractors to balers that package a ton of hay in a single ball. In 1996 alone, the company introduced close to 50 new products and expanded its overseas sales by 31 percent.

Above: Although farm machinery represents the largest segment of Deere & Company's business, it also has a large division of construction equipment, including these front-end loaders. All told, the multinational company had $6 billion in sales in 1996.

Left: A man on a John Deere tractor has become an icon of the American farmer.

Above: The John Deere tractor and plow remains as Deere & Company's core enterprise. The company was first started in the 1830s when John Deere, a 33-year-old blacksmith, reconfigured a discarded mill saw blade into a plow that proved especially effective in digging up dirt on Illinois farms. Sales soared. The company continues to manufacture plows and has diversified into almost all aspects of farming machinery as well as construction and lawn equipment.

Right: A John Deere combine harvester loads wheat onto a truck during the fall harvest in Alberta, Canada.

JOHN DEERE

ABOVE: *A John Deere combine harvests wheat on an Illinois farm as a John Deere tractor waits. Deere & Company manufactures the most tractors and combine harvesters in the United States.*

LEFT: *Deere & Company's agricultural machinery runs the gamut, including this cotton picker emptying its bin into a compactor on a California cotton farm. The company releases as many as 50 new kinds of machines a year.*

Like most multinational manufacturers of heavy equipment, Deere & Company doesn't just build big machinery. Deere & Company also has a financing arm, an insurance group, and a health-care organization, as well as industrial, lawn care, and parts divisions.

FORESTRY EQUIPMENT

▲ A tree harvester operated by a single person can fell, delimb, debark, and cut a 100-foot-tall tree into useable logs in less than 30 seconds, a fraction of the time a team of burly lumberjacks could accomplish the same task with chain saws and muscle.

ABOVE: *After timber has been harvested, the transportation of heavy logs is a significant task. Here a log barge carries a load of logs to an Oregon mill.*

RIGHT: *A log loader, which is very similar to a hydraulic excavator except it has a different attachment, working at the edge of the woods in Olympic Peninsula, Washington.*

Tree Harvester and Forwarder

Mechanization freed loggers from their reliance on human muscle and saw blades to fell trees. Equipped with bulldozers, large chain saws, winches, chains, and log loaders, a logger could clear-cut a wooded parcel in a fraction of the time formerly required.

The problem was that clear-cutting is often an inefficient and environmentally unfriendly way to harvest timber. Using standard equipment for selective cutting was also difficult. Cumbersome equipment scarred standing trees, hurting their future growth potential, and harvesting trees on site was time consuming. The choice confronting a logger was either to make a mess when harvesting trees or to spend a lot of money to accomplish the task neatly.

The advent of tree harvesters and forwarders has helped bridge that gap. Using what is known as cut-to-length technology, a logger can take a tree harvester into the woods to fell, delimb, debark, and cut a full-grown tree in seconds. An articulated forwarder will then lift and carry the logs out of the forest. The leading-edge technology, largely developed in Scandanavia, is far friendlier on the environment and can be applied in all but the most difficult forest conditions.

A 15-ton tree harvester looks similar to a small excavator. Typically mounted on a rugged, articulated tractorlike vehicle, the harvester has a boom and arm with a reach of close to 30 feet that carries a harvesting head. The head is an impressive piece of machinery consisting of a combination of saws, grips, and debarkers.

An operator positions the head at the base of the tree with grippers grasping on to the base. A saw cuts the tree at the base and then lifts it. The machine then pulls the tree through the harvesting head as saws and debarkers remove limbs and bark. When the trunk of the tree reaches a predetermined distance, another saw cuts the trunk and the log falls to the ground. The harvester repeats the process until it consumes the entire tree.

It takes less than 30 seconds to harvest an 80-foot-tall tree with a 2-foot diameter. A computerized measuring system records the number of trees cut; the output in terms of the size, the number of logs, and the amount of pulpwood; the species of the tree; the productivity of the machine; and other information. Tree delimbers and feller-bunchers perform tasks similar to those of tree harvesters.

Having divided the pieces of the tree into usable logs and brush, a forwarder arrives to pick up the logs and carry them out of the forest. A forwarder is essentially a tractor especially designed to maneuver through the rough terrain of woods; it is equipped with a log loader and carriage in back to haul the logs. The combination of a tree harvester and forwarder allows a logger to selectively cut trees on-site without damaging other trees in the forest, compacting the soil, or causing extensive damage to the ecosystem.

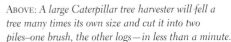

ABOVE: A large Caterpillar tree harvester will fell a tree many times its own size and cut it into two piles—one brush, the other logs—in less than a minute.

ABOVE, INSET: Turn-of-the-century machinery hauls a pile of logs out of an evergreen forest. Some of the early innovations in modern equipment were made specifically for logging. The Lombard Steam Log Hauler, for example, represented in 1901 the first practical use of crawler treads to propel a large machine and was used for hauling lumber over iced roads in the northern United States and Canada.

LEFT: The head of a tree harvester cuts a tree down, debarks it, saws off its limbs, and cuts its trunk into a pile of logs. The operator since in an elevated booth for maximum visibility. This machine is working on the Olympic Peninsula in Washington State.

BOTTOM, LEFT: A Caterpillar Sixty tractor and Williamette Hyster Skidding Arch haul tree-length logs out of the woods in the 1930s. The cumbersomeness of this operation and the destruction that the dragged trunks wreaked on the forest compelled the innovation of modern tree harvesters, which are both more efficient and less harmful to the forest's environment.

RIGHT: A grapple yarder is used for logging on Vancouver Island, Canada.

Tree Chippers

Whole tree chippers will take a 100-foot tree and turn it into a pile of chips in under a minute. Armed with spinning knives inside the machine, chippers slice and dice tree trunks, limbs, and brush up to 30 inches in diameter. Ranging in size from small household chippers that can be easily maneuvered by hand for backyard work to 1,000-horsepower machines, most chippers are towed, although some are self-propelled.

Giant tree chippers are typically used for clearing woods, rights of way, space for pipelines and other purposes that involve the felling of large trees and the disposal of either the entire tree, its limbs, or brush. The chips can be blown onto the ground where they decompose back into the soil. More often,

however, the wooden chips are used commercially for a wide variety of purposes including pulp, fuel for wood-fired cogeneration plants, pressed board, composting, or mulch.

Depending on the size of the wood being chipped, the material is fed into the machine either by hand or with an automatic loader. The larger chippers often have loaders equipped with a grappler to feed the wood into the chipper. As the wood enters the chipper, powerful feeder wheels pull the material into machine and force it into rapidly spinning cyclinders that cut the tree into pieces. Similar to a giant, ultra-fast meat cutter that is tilted on an angle, the tree chippers cylinders cut thin pieces of wood that are then sent flying out through a maneuverable discharge unit. The size of the chips is regulated by how the knives are positioned.

▲ Chips from tree chippers are used as pulp fuel for wood-fired cogeneration plants, pressed board, composting and mulch.

Self-propelled tree chippers have the advantage of being able to be driven directly into the woods to do the chipping on-site rather than having to use a person to operate a skidder, a specially designed vehicle for hauling timber, to retrieve the wooden waste material. Tree Bandit's Model 1900 Whole Tree Chipper, for example, is a large but not gigantic self-propelled machine with a capacity to chip trees up to 19 inches in diameter at a pace of 100 feet per minute. Average production for the machine is between 200 and 250 tons of wood a shift. The machine is mounted on to two 30-inch-wide crawler tracks that give the chipper traction for maneuvering through the rough terrain of the forest but exert a modest 6 pounds of pressure per square inch on the ground below, thereby minimizing soil compression. Stability is enhanced by creating a low center of gravity, and the operator is positioned in front over the infeed area. The swivel discharge can swing on a 220-degree angle, enabling the machine to disperse the chips over a wide area. It weighs 55,000 pounds, and its list price is about $245,000.

Morbark based in Winn, Michigan, builds larger chippers that can consume trees up to 30 inches in diameter. The Morbark Model 30 and 22 RXL Total Chiparvestor units (which are not self-propelled) are motored by engines with up to 800 horsepower, can produce 500 tons (or 1 million pounds) of chips per hour, and have a list price of $350,000. Operated by a single person perched above the machine, the Chiparvestor's boom will literally pick up a fully grown felled adult tree with a 2½-feet-thick trunk, such as a 50-year-old maple tree, place it on its 10-foot infeed, and spew the wood out of its hydraulic swivel discharge as an enormous pile of wooden chips in a matter of seconds.

FACING PAGE, TOP: *A modestly sized tree chipper on tracks, the Model 1900 Track Bandit by Bandit Industries can travel into the forest to chip trees and brush. The crawlers are long and wide to reduce ground pressure and provide stability to the machine.*

FACING PAGE, BOTTOM: *Tree chippers and tub grinders are capable of making heaping piles of wood chips in a matter of hours. The wooden chips are used commercially for pulp, fuel at wood-fire co-generation plants, pressed board, composting, and mulch.*

Tree Spades

Instead of decimating a tree, giant tree spades remove trees for replanting elsewhere. Gargantuan in scale, they are mounted on top of trucks that both maneuver the machinery and move the tree for transplanting.

One of the biggest, if not the biggest, tree spades is the TS-9400 Tree Spade by Vermeer Manufacturing Company. The machine consists of four mammoth steel spades that are plunged into the earth in a circular pattern around the tree. Each spade is almost 6 feet long, and the entire mechanism weighs 22,500 pounds. Vermeer recommends using the machine for trees whose diameter is between 9 and 12 inches. The scoop a giant ball of dirt at the base of the tree that is almost 8 feet in diameter and more than 5 feeÆt deep. Depending on the soil and moisture level, the ball will weigh in the vicinity of 12,000 pounds. A hydraulic system powers the machine, applying pressure of up to 3,000 pounds per square inch. The machine requires a truck that is at least 29 tons and has a 20-foot-long frame from which to operate.

▲ The largest tree chippers will consume and digest trees with trunks as thick as 30 inches and generate up to 1 million pounds of chips in a shift. They weigh up to 72,000 pounds, boast large hydraulic booms and 800-horsepower engines, and reduce trees to piles of 5/8-inch-thick chips.

SPECIALIZED EQUIPMENT

Most heavy equipment is used for pretty generic purposes. The machines dig holes, lift heavy materials, haul objects short distances, and knock things over. These are timeless activities. But as times have changed, so too have machines. Modern equipment has been made increasingly efficient and powerful, and its purposes have become more refined and specialized. While the costs of creating new machines for narrowly focused purposes usually precludes the building of specialized giant machines, there are some exceptions. When NASA engineers needed a transporter for space rockets, they spared no expense to build the NASA Space Shuttle Crawler-Transporter.

The massive NASA crawler-transporter positions the space shuttle into place at its launch pad at the Kennedy Space Center in Florida.

New categories of equipment are coming into existence that are often derived from refitted existing machines. Twenty-five years ago, the terms heavy equipment and environmental movement were never used in the same sentence unless it was in reference to their conflict. But today's massive recycling and reclamation projects could not be done without heavy equipment. Other types of equipment are completely new. The beginnings of human space exploration have created an entirely new universe for equipment manufacturers to come up with new tools and ways to accomplish tasks in a gravity-free environment. On the other side of the equation, space has also allowed engineers to develop new and ingenious ways to improve the use of equipment here on Earth. Satellites are guiding heavy equipment with incredible precision, even allowing machines to operate without drivers.

SHREDDER

"When it's all done, you don't know if it started out as a car or a refrigerator."

—Tom Dueley

As a teenager in the 1930s, Alton S. Newell dismantled cars the old-fashioned way. Armed with a sledgehammer, wrench, chisel, and axes, he would take about 10 hours to scrap a junked car. There had to be a better way.

More than 30 years later and after a career in the scrap business, Newell devised a new, efficient, if intimidating, way to reduce cars into scrap metal for recycling. The Newell Shredder fed a car into a shredding machine armed with hammers and discs and driven by a 500-horsepower motor. In less than 10 minutes, the car was shredded into small pieces.

Since then, the equipment has both been recognized by the American Society of Mechanical Engineers as a national historic landmark and been enhanced by Newell Industries, as well as several competitors in the shredding industry. The system that Newell developed in 1965 avoided pollution caused by previous methods that burned nonmetallic parts to remove them from the processing. It allowed the anchored system to reject unshreddable scrap, used a smaller, more affordable motor, and discharged scrap in a way that eliminated the need for large foundations.

Newell's largest machines today have motors that range from 1,000 to 6,000 horsepower. After removing the engine, battery, and gas tank, a Newell Shredder today can pulverize an average-size car into 6-by-6-inch pieces of metal in less than 30 seconds.

"It's basically done with brute force," says Tom Dueley, a sales engineer with the company. "The first time you see it, it's very scary. You don't even want to think about what's going on inside."

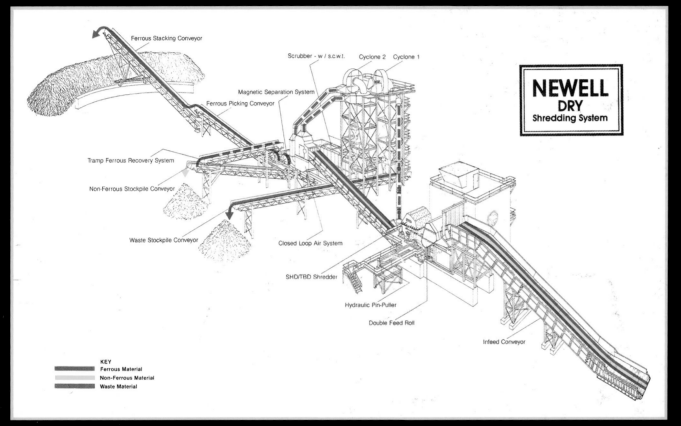

NEWELL
DRY
Shredding System

Ferrous Stacking Conveyor

Scrubber - w / s.c.w.t.   Cyclone 2   Cyclone 1

Magnetic Separation System

Ferrous Picking Conveyor

Tramp Ferrous Recovery System

Non-Ferrous Stockpile Conveyor

Waste Stockpile Conveyor

Closed Loop Air System

SHD/TBD Shredder

Hydraulic Pin-Puller

Double Feed Roll

Infeed Conveyor

KEY
Ferrous Material
Non-Ferrous Material
Waste Material

▲ Hammer heads tipped with manganese travelling at speeds of up to 250 miles per hour will shred a car into bits and pieces of metal in 30 seconds

The size of the vehicle, or other types of material such as large appliances and light iron scrap, to be shredded is limited by the 104-inch-wide entrance to the shredder. As a conveyor belt carries the material into the shredder, a rotor consisting of steel discs and up to ten manganese steel hammers lop off pieces of material. The rotor turns at a rate of 600 rotations per minute with the heads of the hammers traveling at speeds up to 250 miles per hour.

The smaller shredded material falls out of the shredder housing area through a grate and onto a conveyor belt below while the larger pieces are spun through again. Pieces that are simply too big to reduce are sent through a reject door. How small the shredded material is depends on the size of the holes in the grate below. The pieces can be as small as 3 by4 inches. The conveyor belt carres the material through a variety of magnetic separation systems to segregate the different types of metals for recycling.

Depending on the size of the machine used, a shredder will process as much as 150 tons of scrap metal per hour. The cost of the shredders ranges from $1 million to $5 million.

ABOVE: *A crane with a magnetic head works in a scrap-metal pile at a recycling center.*

LEFT: *A grab lifts recycling sheet metal waste from an auto manufacturing plant for reprocessing.*

BOTTOM, INSET: *A load of recyclable cans is lifted high above the ground by an electromagnetic crane.*

Brimming with 56 carbide-tipped knives, the Morbark Waste Recycler will reduce all types of wood waste into chips, including stumps 8 feet in diameter, at a rate of 20 to 30 tons per hour.

Recycling Equipment

With the rise of the environmental movement starting in the 1960s and the realization of the benefits derived from recycled materials, an entire new category of heavy machinery has emerged. Recycling equipment is a rapidly growing and changing arena. From small machines that pulverize glass bottles one at a time to magnetic sorters to giant car crushers, recycling equipment encompasses a wide range of types of equipment. The purpose of the machinery is to sort materials, reduce them, and reconfigure them into manageable forms, whether it is chips of wood, rubber shreds, or bales of metal.

What equipment is used by different companies for different purposes depends entirely on the kinds of material being processed. The types of material that need to be processed for recycling include tires, bottles, cans, cars, paper, plastic, demolition debris, wood, glass, metals, newspapers, and several other products. The choices in how to best utilize a combination of conveyor belts, screens, magnetic sorters, shredders, balers, chippers, hammermills, strippers, crushers, tire shredders, paper shredders, bottle busters, shears, granulators, vibrating feeders, and pulverizers to process these different categories seems almost infinite.

Some of this equipment is immense and very powerful. The Michigan manufacturer Morbark makes the mobile 40-ton Model 1500 Tub Grinder with a 15-foot tub that decimates organic waste into pulverized chips. Driven by a 1,000-horsepower engine, its hammermill rotor consisting of 28 steel-fixed, 36-inch-diameter hammers that grind wood waste of almost any size at a rate of up to 500 cubic yards per hour, or enough organic waste to fill four conventional tractor trailer trucks. The pulverized material can be used as mulch, fuel chips, compost, and other purposes. Other types of shredders will reduce tires into 1 1/2-inch rubber chips, bulky metal into small pieces, hard-plastic items into granulated chunks.

Another category of equipment frequently used in recycling is compactors and bailers. Powerful engines compress everything from tin cans to car bodies into bales of metal or simply compress waste in large containers to reduce the bulk. Other ways to reduce the size of materials include drum-and-roll crushers that simply smash items as conveyors force them through. Most recycling equipment is usually used in permanent plants that process large amounts of materials. The different types of equipment, however, are often mounted on wheels for on-site work. In some cases companies have put together very complicated networks of conveyor belts, crushers, screens, hoppers, power jacks, rotors, feeders, and other items on to a trailer bed to serve as mobile recycling and crushing plants.

RIGHT: *Piles of wooden debris are dumped into the tub of a tub grinder, which generates as much as 500 cubic yards of mulch an hour, or enough to fill four tractor trailer trucks. This machine in Michigan is grinding cedar planks into mulch.*

MILITARY EQUIPMENT

ABOVE: *The Twenty-first U.S. Engineer Corps prepares for laying down a temporary runway for a portable landing field during World War II. The equipment includes two Caterpillar D-7 tractors pulling two LeTourneau Carryalls to scrape and grade the land. LeTourneau, Inc., made 10,785 Carryalls for the U.S. Army during World War II.*

ABOVE, INSET: *In addition to the usual duties of a mobile crane, the military often uses cranes to remove damaged or destroyed vehicles, planes, or other weaponry. Other types of recovery equipment have included crash pushers that shoved downed airplanes off runways and a landing craft retriever to salvage beached or capsized amphibious landing craft.*

LEFT: *An M-60 tank doubles as a bulldozer for field operations. In the Persian Gulf War, U.S. tanks and bulldozer buried Iraqi positions by shoving mounds of dirt into their entrenched positions.*

The history of heavy equipment and military equipment have often overlapped. The needs of armies have pushed the capability of civil engineers to come up with new, fast ways to accomplish objectives such as building bridges, toppling ships, moving earth, and other goals. Not coincidentally, innovations in military equipment technology during wartime have often spurred the development of civilian equipment. The use of tractors in World War I, for example, served as an important catalyst for the tractor industry after the war. And on the other side of the equation, heavy equipment used for peaceful purposes sometimes inspire soldiers to apply more lethal uses. The invention of the modern tank came as a direct result of a visit by British officers to a Caterpillar tractor factory during World War I.

Archimedes' Ship-Shaking Machine

One of the great engineering minds of all time belonged to the Greek scientist Archimedes. His inventions included the Archimedes' screw, a spiral-shaped water lift that is still used today, as well as levers that could move huge objects with relatively light force applied. "Give me something to stand on and I will move the earth," he proclaimed. In 215 B.C., Archimedes applied his genius to the defense of the besieged and outmanned Sicilian city of Syracuse from the Roman army and navy. He not only devised catapults to fire missiles and giant stones on enemy troops to great effect, but also invented a crane that destroyed Roman ships. Known as the "ship-shaking machine" or "claws," the giant crane reached over the city wall and into the harbor with a large metal claw suspended by chains from a long wooden beam. It is unclear precisely how it was achieved, but the claw would clutch onto the prow of the ship. The weighted end of the beam inside Syracuse would then be pulled down with levers and the claw would pull the ship out of the water. "A ship was frequently lifted up to a great height in the air—a dreadful thing to behold—and was rolled to and fro, and kept swinging, until the mariners were all thrown out, when at length it was dashed against the rocks, or was dropped," the Greek historian Plutarch wrote.

Battering Rams

Battering rams were used by armies from ancient times until the advent of gunpowder. The Assyrians in about 800 B.C. were among the first to build battering rams by erecting protective structures mounted on wheels to approach an enemy fortification and attempt to knock it down with either a flat-ended battering ram or massive lances. To prevent defenders from pouring missiles, hot oil, and incendiary objects onto the mobile machine, armored protection was added and towers were erected from which archers would shoot arrows. The siege engines were further developed over time to improve their mobility and protective measures. Sometimes the machines were used in open battlefields, as well, because the armored engines offered protection to the fighters inside.

Bulldozers

Bulldozers have played a major role in modern warfare. From moving earth on the Western Front in World War I to clearing

The military is almost as much an earthmoving operation as it is a fighting one. A front-end loader in camouflage paint moves unloads a pile of sand to be hauled away.

A medium-sized World War I tank crosses a trench. British engineers were inspired to invent tanks after observing the Caterpillar tractor factory during World War I. The rugged crawler-tractors served as a model for the military weapon.

In addition to the usual duties of a mobile crane, the military often uses cranes to remove damaged or destroyed vehicles, planes, or other weaponry. Other types of recovery equipment have included crash pushers that shoved downed airplanes off runways and a landing craft retriever to salvage beached or capsized amphibious landing craft.

debris from bombed-out cities in World War II to burying Iraqi defensive forces in the Persian Gulf War, the combination of a powerful engine and massive metal blade has proven to be remarkably useful in the rigors of combat. No less a figure than U.S. tank commander in World War II General George Patton observed that given the choice between using tanks or bulldozers for a beachhead invasion, he would go with the bulldozers. In fact, in the 1944 Allied invasion of Normandy bulldozers were used to literally smother enemy machine-gun nests housed in concrete bunkers. Almost 40 years later, U.S. combat engineer vehicles (CEV), which are essentially lightly armed bulldozers, and tanks equipped with dozer blades buried entrenched Iraqi soldiers by shoving huge mounds of earth into the trenches as machine-gun fire pinned the enemy troops down. The line between tanks and bulldozers sometimes blurs, such as the heavily armed M1A1 tank, which is fitted with mine plow that digs through the dirt at a speed of up to 10 miles per hour clearing mines.

Tactical Crushers

The U.S. Army Corps of Engineers turned to a new category of military equipment called *tactical crushers* in the 1960s in Vietnam. Mired in the jungles of Southeast Asia, the military wanted to clear wide swaths of buffer zones and security strips. Working with R. G. LeTourneau, Inc., the army commissioned a 97-ton Transphibian Tactical Crusher with 14 wide hexagon rollers designed to crush any and all trees, underbrush, and other vegetation in its path. Although it was capable of crossing rivers and swamps, the machine was not effective in combat and broke down frequently. In place of a crusher, the army fitted giant Rome K/G clearing blades to Caterpillar D7E and Allis-Chalmers HD-16M tractors to accomplish the same job. One thousand of these "Rome Plows" were used for land clearing operations during the Vietnam War.

Recovery Equipment

Starting in World War II, an entire new category of heavy military equipment was developed to salvage or dispose armored vehicles, planes, and other types of weaponry. Crash cranes were built for use on U.S. Navy aircraft carriers to clear the decks of damaged airplanes as well as lift heavy materials. Larger bomber cranes were used by the U.S. Air Force for similar tasks on its air bases. After the war, the U.S. Army commissioned R.G. LeTourneau, Inc., to design a larger, more powerful "crash pusher." The company came up with the LeTourneau CP-1 Crash Pusher, 67-foot-long, 67-ton giant bulldozer operated by a 600-horsepower Cummins VT-12 engine, mounted on six 10-foot-diameter tires, and armed with a 13-by-5-foot bulldozer blade. Able to travel up to 25 miles per hour, it could remove a 200-ton bomber from a runway in 20 minutes. The army also had LeTourneau design a Landing Craft Retriever to salvage beached or capsized amphibious landing craft. Hoisted on four 10-foot-diameter tires, the 75-foot-long, 38-foot-wide machine was essentially a large metal frame on wheels with two cranes for lifting. It could operate in water up to 8 feet deep, and lift up to 67 tons and was run by a 230-horsepower motor.

NASA SPACE SHUTTLE CRAWLER-TRANSPORTER

The space shuttle Discovery rolls atop the NASA crawler-transporter onto Launch Pad 39A at the Kennedy Space Center. The crawlers on the machine are each 41 feet long and 10 feet high. Each shoe on the crawler weighs a ton.

LEFT: *This view from above of the NASA crawler-transporter shows the scale of the massive machine. The machine is 131 feet long and 114 feet wide with a deck that is 90 feet wide on each side, or the dimensions of a baseball diamond.*

ABOVE: *It takes the NASA crawler-transporter about 6 hours to carry the space shuttle and return to base. The machine travels over a specially constructed 130-foot-wide roadway that connects the Vehicle Assembly Building to two launch sites. Depending on which launch site is used, the distance traveled is either 3.4 or 4.2 miles.*

▲ Powered by a total of 5,500 horsepower, the crawler-transporter carries 11 million pounds of steel at a top speed of 1 mile per hour. It typically takes 6 hours for it to carry its load to the launch pad and back on a 130-foot-wide road specially built for the massive machine.

Before NASA's space shuttle can blast off into space at almost unbelievable speeds, it first needs to be crept into position for liftoff. For this one and only purpose the National Aeronautics and Space Administration (NASA) commissioned Marion Power Shovel Company to build two crawler-transporters for $13.6 million.

The vehicles, nicknamed "Hans" and "Franz," are a curious blend of sheer size and delicate precision. The vehicles weigh 6 million pounds each. The space shuttle and mobile platform combined are 11 million pounds. At the same time, the crawler-transporter needs to have the agility to place the multi-billion-dollar equipment in the exact position from which to launch its journey into the cosmos.

Each crawler-transporter is 131 feet long, 114 feet wide, and 20 feet high. The deck that holds the upright space shuttle and mobile launcher platform is the size of a baseball diamond (90 feet per side). The vehicle, which travels at a top speed of 2 miles per hour without its load, moves on four double-tracked crawlers, each 10 feet high and 41 feet long. Each shoe on the crawler weighs a ton. The vehicle is powered by two 2,750-horsepower diesel engines that drive four 1,000-kilowatt generators, which in turn power 16 traction motors.

A leveling system keeps the top of the space shuttle vertical as the crawler-transporter maneuvers down a specially built roadway and a ramp (whose incline is 5 percent) leading to the launch pads. The system also keeps its load level as it raises and lowers the space shuttle into position. The top of the space shuttle thus always stays within the width of a basketball of being perfectly vertical.

When called to duty, the vehicle carries the space shuttle from the Vehicle Assembly Building (one of the world's largest buildings at 129 million cubic feet) to one of two launch sites 3.4 and 4.2 miles away. The vehicle travels on a 130-foot-wide roadway—as broad as an eight-lane highway. The road surface consists of river gravel that is 8 inches thick on the curves and 4 inches on the straightaway sections.

When carrying its load, the crawler-transporter never exceeds 1 mile per hour. It usually takes about 5 hours to bring the space shuttle to its launching site. Upon arriving at the launch pad, technicians and engineers position the space shuttle for liftoff. As the space shuttle prepares to shoot for the stars, the crawler-transporter trudges back to its parking area.

CANADARM

With Earth providing a dramatic backdrop, astronauts from the Endeavor space shuttle use the Canadarm, or RMS, as a work platform to repair the Hubble Space Telescope in December 1993.

Strictly speaking, the Canadarm is not heavy equipment. Only 902 pounds, it cannot even lift its own weight here on earth. But in the weightless atmosphere of space the Canadarm is a muscle-bound lifter, capable of catching, maneuvering and releasing a 65,000-pound satellite.

In its 16-year life, the Canadarm has performed about 50 missions. It helped rescue the Solar Max satellite in 1984 and retrieved the Hubble Space Telescope in 1993.

The Canadarm, also known as the Shuttle Remote Manipulator System (SRMS), was built in 1981 by Spar Aerospace Limited under the direction of the National Research Council of Canada (now the Canadian Space Agency) for NASA's Space Shuttle Program. It cost $120 million to develop the first arm and $25 million for the four subsequent arms used by NASA. One of the Canadarms was destroyed when the space shuttle Challenger exploded in 1986.

Designed like a human arm, it has three joints: a shoulder with two degrees of freedom, an elbow joint with one degree of freedom, and the wrist joint with three degrees of freedom. The arm is maneuvered by computer and can either be operated manually or with computer automation. A knob operated with the left hand controls the arm and control stick for the right hand controls the end of the arm. A trigger on the right-hand control is used to squeeze and release the arm's gripper, or hand. Unloaded the arm moves at a speed of up to 2 feet per second, loaded it slows down to 2.4 inches a second.

The Canadarm is specially designed to withstand the rigors and peculiarities of operating in space on a space shuttle. The arm, which is 50 feet long, is made of lightweight but tough materials such as titanium, stainless steel, and graphite epoxy to weather the freezing temperatures of space. An insulated blanket with thermostatically controlled heaters keeps the equipment at acceptable temperatures near 0 degrees Celsius. Conversely, the blanket protects the metal from the heat of the sun's powerful rays.

Zero gravity in space meant engineers had to design thrusters to counter the impact of the arm catching and releasing objects. The force of the small jets and thrusters are precisely coordinated with a computer to ensure that the space shuttle is not thrown off course when it retrieves and maneuvers a satellite.

More than 300 wires are intertwined along the length of the arm to control its movements. The length of two telephone poles and 25 inches in diameter, it weighs 10 percent of what a wooden log of similar dimensions would weigh. The amount of electricity needed to power the arm is minimal, about the equivalent to operating an electric tea kettle.

Tasks that the Canadarm has performed include placing satellites in orbit, making rendezvous with malfunctioning satellites, truss construction, serving as a platform for astronauts on spacewalks, docking with space stations, and examining the skin of the space shuttle with a remote television camera eye. In a pinch, the machine has also been called on to unclog waste water drains, knock off ice clinging to orbiters, and loosen a jammed solar array panel.

The groundbreaking robotic technology developed for the Canadarm has been used for several other earthbound purposes. Similar manipulators are used to handle radioactive and other hazardous materials and servicing nuclear power stations. New innovations in robotic technology have been applied to the Canadarms, which have been constantly upgraded. The existing Canadarm is being strengthened to carry even larger loads. In the meantime two new robotic systems are being built by Spar as Canada's contribution for a planned international space station. One is a bigger and improved Canadarm that will be 60 feet long. The other is a two-armed robotic system designed for smaller and more precise tasks than the Canadarm.

LEFT: *An astronaut practices using the Canadarm, or RMS, from the space shuttle.*

BELOW: *In November 1984, astronauts used the Shuttle Remote Manipulator System (RMS) to rescue and repair the Wester satellite. They also took it upon themselves to see if any passing spaceships might want to purchase the damaged satellite.*

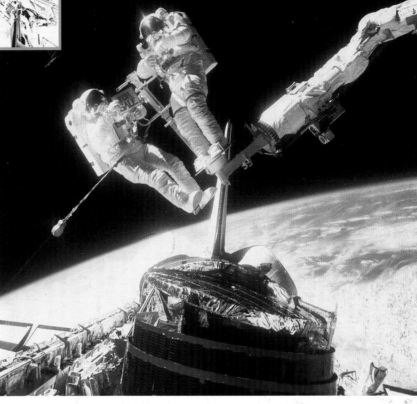

▲ Canadarm has the dimensions of two wooden telephone poles laid out end to end but is one-tenth the weight. It can maneuver an object in space the size and weight of a fully loaded bus. Kept at about 0 degrees Celsius in space, it has operated successfully in temperatures ranging from minus-36 to 60 degrees on earth.

Comic books have offered some of the most peculiar types of equipment for dastardly purposes. Here, The Fox, The Shark, and The Vulture drive "The Burrow Machine" to tunnel under Gotham City and break into banks, much to the chagrin of the caped crusaders Batman and Robin.

FICTIONAL EQUIPMENT

The movie Alien was the first of three science-fiction horror movies that take place in mining stations scattered across the universe. The films' creators invented all sorts of mining equipment for the space-age story, including this desolate outpost on an obscure planet.

From taming giant beasts to devising bizarre machinery, the human imagination has constantly stretched the boundaries of the improbable ways to perform tasks that heavy equipment accomplishes. For centuries, engineers, builders, and inventors have plumbed the depths of their fertile brains to come up with different—and sometimes outrageous—ways to lift, move, dig, carry, build, shove, and otherwise process materials. More recently, science fiction writers and artists, starting with Jules Verne in the nineteenth century, have let their imaginations run amuck to devise outrageous machines and tactics to perform the same tasks. These imaginative thinkers have often proved to be more like prophets than like cranks. Many a peculiar machine that was once thought to be a laughable, if not impossible, dream proved to be a blueprint for what lay in store for the future. The line between fiction and reality blurred.

As one amazing invention followed another starting in the nineteenth century, people began to realize that what had once seemed impossible, all of sudden was quite plausible. Who could even have imagined taking a photograph before the camera was invented or destroying an entire city with a single bomb before the advent of the atomic bomb? Unencumbered by the feasible, imaginative minds came up with outrageous notions of how to perform extraordinary tasks such as flying.

Perhaps the quaintest category in this realm is the ability to enlist giant animals to assist us humans. In the television cartoon show *The Flintstones*, Fred Flinstone rides a giant dinosaur to do his work in a quarry, mammoth elephants serve as fire hydrants, and rhinoceroses are bulldozers. Elephants in the Disney movie *Dumbo* are called upon to erect the circus tent. And in the annual Christmas *Rudolph the Red-Noised Reindeer* television special, the Abominable Snowman is tamed into placing the star at the top of Santa Claus's giant Christmas tree.

Since the 1930s, comic-book writers and artists have had a field day with heavy equipment. Usually superheroes are endowed with the sorts of power and strength that machinery has. Superman is "more powerful than a locomotive," for example. But the writers and artists often came up with bizarre equipment, such as "The Burrow Machine," a "fantastic crime machine" that Batman and Robin battled. A cross between a car, a tractor, and a giant screw, this machine was used by The Fox, The Shark, and The Vulture to tunnel under the earth to break into banks. In other instances, superheroes and supervillains used heavy equipment to accomplish their own tasks. Superman took a giant scoop to gather the fragments that make up Saturn's rings. The Green Hornet used his magical powers to operate a bulldozer from afar with his ring, which as ludicrous as it may sound is not too far off from what today's Global Positioning System (GPS) networks can do with computers.

Movies, however, are where the imagination and equipment intersect in the most fantastic ways, particularly with the advent of special-effects technologies. Science fiction and Godzilla-type monster movies after World War II frequently enlisted large-scale equipment in their plots to try to slay giant creatures. Although it was usually a slightly different category than heavy equipment, Q's inventions in the James Bond movies of the 1960s employed ingenious devices to convert ordinary items such as watches and cars into multifaceted machines. Starting in the 1970s, however, fictional equipment took on a whole new dimension. Using special effects, moviemakers could create machines that almost took on characters of their own, especially in futuristic movies that took place in space. All sorts of made-up machines were used in the *Star Wars* trilogy, from robots that performed manual (and intellectual) tasks to giant land battleships that lurched forward on metal legs. In the *Alien* movies, actress Sigourney Weaver more than once used a machine with giant metal booms and claws that served almost as extensions of her own limbs to battle the voracious monster "Mother." When you see what robotic engineers have designed for use in space and underwater work, and what they plan to do in the future to improve these machines, the day may not be as far off when today's sort of fictional equipment is, in fact, very much like real equipment.

The inventive minds of the television cartoon producers at Hanna-Barbara came up with all sorts of clever ways to accomplish tasks in the cartoon shows The Flintstones *and* The Jetsons. *While prehistoric animals such as dinosaurs worked rock quarries in* The Flintstones, *futuristic equipment was employed for pedestrian uses in* The Jetsons, *such as a conveyor belt used for walking the dog.*

Sigourney Weaver armed herself with futuristic interplanetary mining equipment in the movie Aliens *to battle the monstrous alien "Mother."*

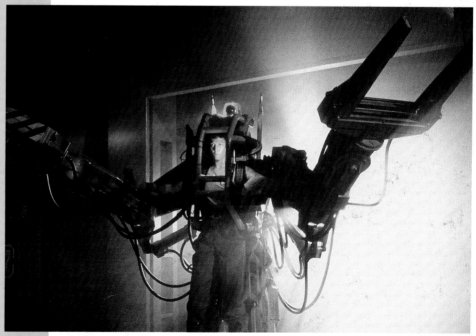

The Future
(or Look, No Hands!)

The future in heavy equipment lies not so much in bigger machines, but smarter ones. Advanced electronic systems, satellite frequencies, and lasers are ushering a new era of increasing sophistication into industries historically marked by brute force. Economic pressures combined with the advent of new information technologies have forced changes in the way heavy equipment is used. Companies are looking for ways to cut costs and exploit their resources more efficiently. Automation allows them to both reduce labor costs and perform tasks with greater precision.

Giant driverless trucks, satellite-guided drills, and bulldozers directed by lasers will all be a part of a rapidly approaching future. Rudimentary versions of all three of these examples are already under way.

The Global Positioning System (GPS) has unleashed the potential of automation and enhanced performance. Twenty-four satellites orbit the globe sending earthbound navigational signals. Receivers interpret the intersection of the signals to precisely locate positions. Developed by the United States Defense Department, GPS earned worldwide fame in 1991 for the extraordinary precision with which it guided missiles during the Persian Gulf War. Since then, many civilian applications for the technology have been explored and nurtured. The applications range from surveying to agriculture to strip-mining.

Caterpillar has developed an automated mining truck using GPS technology. A manned truck drives a predetermined route that is recorded using GPS. The data are transmitted to a computer that converts the information into a route file that then directs an unmanned truck to follow the same route. Front- and rear-mounted radar units detect obstacles and signal the truck to stop. Loader and crusher operators use control panels to signal the truck to move into position in staging areas, similar to children directing radio-operated models.

Another increasingly common application of GPS is the guidance of mining drills. Computers in the machine will direct it where to go and perform its tasks virtually without assistance from an operator. Similar to the automated trucks, the computer-driven equipment is not impaired by inclement weather or the imperfections or fatigue of the operater.

In addition, new electronic systems are able to analyze and assess the health of machines to maximize efficiency. For example, Caterpillar has created the Vital Information Management System that constantly monitors the performance of the autonomous mining truck.

Lasers are another new technology being developed; they are being used to assist heavy equipment such as graders, bulldozers, and other machines in precisely executing tasks. The high-tech equipment tells operators exactly how deep to make cuts and the precise grade of the work. Lasers have also allowed pavers to lay asphalt with exact precision.

Although it will be several years before human judgment takes a back seat to automated machinery, many people in the business foresee the day of their open-pit mining operation with no crew present and the computer-driven bulldozer on a construction site.

▲ GPS satellites orbit the earth at an altitude of 12,454 miles, circling the globe every 12 hours. The most sophisticated GPS navigational equipment has an accuracy of 1 inch and will gain a fix on the location several times a second.

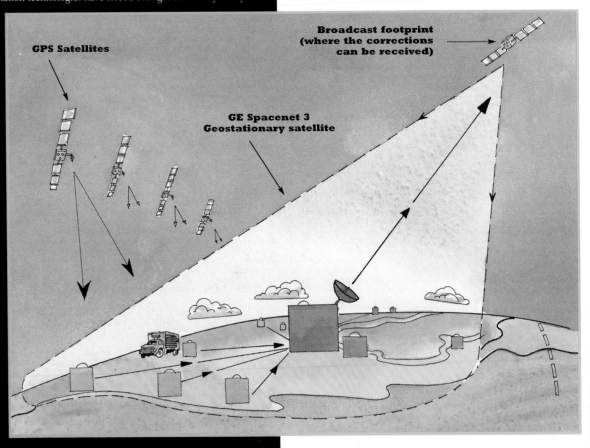

GPS Satellites

Broadcast footprint (where the corrections can be received)

GE Spacenet 3 Geostationary satellite

▲ The Russians have developed a satellite constellation similar to GPS, called GLONASS, with 48 satellites, giving the system the potential for better user-to-satellite geometry and more options in the event of environmental obstructions.

This book is dedicated to
Andrew Bruun, and Bitsy, Christopher, and Lindsey Keith.

Acknowledgments

Many people have helped make this book possible. From enthusiasts of heavy equipment to company employees who have gone beyond the call of duty, several individuals have given their time and expertise. They have shown great patience and have been extremely generous with their time. We are very grateful for their assistance.

We would like to acknowledge several people, in particular, for their contribution to this book. They include: Erik Andersen of Tower Cranes of America; Anthony Barnaba and Robert Harrison of Blueline Designs; Betty Becker of Big Brutus, Inc.; Peter Benger and Merilee Hunt of Liebherr; John G. Blicha of Joy Mining Machinery; Bill Bontemps and Russell Walker of Komatsu America International; David J. Bowler; Peter Causer of O & K; Jarrett Cowden of Vermeer Manufacturing; Mark Deitz of P & H Mining Equipment; Tom Deuley of Newell Industries; Daren Drollinger of the The Equipment Institute; Gideon Garcia of Gray Line of Alaska; Derek Gentile; Thomas Gething of Atlas Copco Robbins Inc.; Randy Govier of Bucyrus International Inc.; Helmut Kircheis of Rheinbraun Hauptverwaltung; Jed Lipsky; Donna Mattoon; Hans W. Schellhorn; Mark Sprouls of Caterpillar; Trax Incorporated, and Tom Woodfin.

In addition, this book could not have been done without the vision of JP Leventhal and the talents of the book editor Pamela Horn, copy editor Richard Gallin, proofreader Joe Arsenault, art director Liz Trovato, production manager Tim Stauffer, illustrator Lamont O'Neil, and photo researchers Maisie Todd and Diana Gongora.

We are indebted to all of these people and many others for their expertise and help. They deserve the credit for all that is good in this book.

June 30, 1997

Bibliography

Acona, George. *Monster Movers.* New York: E. P. Dutton, 1983.

The Caterpillar Story. Peoria, Illinois: Caterpillar, Inc., 1990.

Cohrs, Heinz-Herbert. *500 Years of Earthmoving.* Southfields, England: KHL International, 1997.

Construction Equipment Magazine

Durst, W., and and W. Vogt. *Bucket Wheel Excavator.* Clausthal-Zellerfeld, Germany: Trans Tech Publications, 1988.

Engineering and Mining Journal

Equipment Today Magazine

Equipment World Magazine

Eurotunnel, The Illustrated Journal. New York: HarperCollins, 1995.

Forbes, R. J. *Studies in Ancient Technology.* Leiden: E. J. Brill, 1965.

Genat, Robert. *Road Construction.* Osceola, Wisc.: Motorbooks International, 1995.

Gowenlock, Philip G. *The LeTourneau Legend: The History of R. G. LeTourneau, Inc., 1920-1970.* Brisbane, Australia: Paddington Publications, 1996.

Halberstadt, Hans. *Demolition Equipment.* Osceola, Wisc.: Motorbooks International, 1996.

Halberstadt, Hans. *Giant Dump Trucks.* Osceola, Wisc.: Motorbooks International, 1995.

Highway and Heavy Construction Magazine

James, Peter, and Nick Thorpe. *Ancient Inventions.* New York: Ballantine Books, 1994.

Landels, J. G., *Engineering in the Ancient World.* Berkeley, Calif.: University of California Press, 1978.

Leffingwell, Randy. *Caterpillar.* Osceola, Wisc.: Motorbooks International, 1994.

Marsh, Barbara. *A Corporate Tragedy: The Agony of International Harvester Company.* Garden City, N.Y.: Doubleday & Co., 1985.

McCullogh, David. *The Path Between the Seas: The Creation of the Panama Canal, 1870–1914.* New York: Simon and Schuster, 1977.

Mills, Robert K. *Implement & Tractor: Reflections on 100 Years of Farm Equipment:* Overlank Park, Kan.: Intertec Publishing, 1986.

Mining Engineering Magazine

Moorhouse, Robert. *The Illustrated History of Tractors.* Edison, N.J.: Chartwell Books, 1996.

Northern Logger and Timber Processor Magazine

Orlemann, Eric C. *Giant Earth-Moving Equipment.* Osceola, Wisc.: Motorbooks International, 1995.

Poirier, Rene. *The Fifteen Wonders of the World.* London: Victor Gollancz, 1961.

Pollard, Michael. *Amazing Structures.* New York: Barnes & Noble Books, 1996.

Pripps, Robert N. *Farm Crawlers.* Osceola, Wisc.: Motorbooks International, 1994.

Sargent, Sam, and Michael Alves. *Bulldozers.* Osceola, Wisc.: Motorbooks International, 1994.

Shapiro, Howard I. *Cranes and Derricks.* New York: McGraw Hill, 1980.

Spence, Clark C. *The Northern Gold Fleet: Twentieth-Century Gold Dredging in Alaska.* Chicago: University of Illinois Press, 1996.

Thrasher, Barbara. *Earth Movers.* New York: Crescent Books, 1997.

Wilson, Mitchell. *American Science and Invention.* New York: Bonanza Books, 1969.

World Crane Guide 1995/96. Southfields, England: International Cranes, 1996.

Photography Credits

AGCO: p.99, bottom right

Alaska Stock Images: Clark Mishler, p.80, top

American Electric Power: p.57; p.10, top

Anderson, E.M.: p.50, top left

Archive: Reuters/Robert NG, p.15top, inset; Volkmar Hentzel, p.97, right; Orville Snider, p.97, bottom; Lambert, p.104, top left

Bandit Industries: p.108, top

Baraban, Joe: cover; p.40,bottom right; p.41, right; p.83, top

Benson, Gary J.: p.61, bottom inset; p.73, bottom

Big Brutus, Inc.: p.54

Brown Brothers: p.6, bottom left; p.6–7, top center; p.12, right inset; p.39, top; p.75; p.82; p.84–85; p.84, bottom inset; p.96, top center; p.97, center; p.99, top; p.100, bottom center; p.104, top inset; p.105, right inset; p.116; p.117, center

Bucyrus International, Inc.: p.66

Camerique: p.46, inset

Caterpillar: p.18, bottom; p.26; *p.27, bottom;*p.37, inset; p.63, top; p.65, right; p.107, bottom left; p.22-23, bottom, center

Cavanaugh, Dan J., Co.: p.28

Cox, Dennis: p.11, top inset

Cox, Tim C.: p.61, bottom, top right; p.66, inset; p.67, inset; p.78; p.79, center inset, right inset

D.C. Comics: p.122, inset

DDB Stock Photo: Suzanne L. Murphy, p.13, top inset

Deere, John & Co.: p.98, inset; p.104, right, left, center

Everett Collection: p.122; p.123, bottom, top

Fotopic: p.39, inset

FPG: Billy E. Barnes, p.23, center, inset; Frank A. Cezus, p.24, inset; Stephen Simpson, p.25, center inset; Walter Bibikow, p.49, bottom; Steven Gottlieb, p.3

Gomaco Corp.: p.31

H. Armstrong Roberts: p.6,right center, top left, bottom right; p.8, right; p.9, top inset; p.18,top; p.19,bottom; p.22,top inset, bottom left; p.24; p.25, bottom; p.30, top; p.31, bottom inset, top inset; p.32, bottom; p.35,bottom; Joe Baraban, p.38,bottom left, bottom right, top; Brinkman/Bavaria, p.72, bottom inset; Gerard Fritz, p.41l, bottom; Kenneth Garrett, p.72, top inset; p.80-81, p.81, inset, p.90, p.91, inset; p.91; Wendell Metzen, p.4l, top, center inset, contents; p.44, bottom left, bottom right; p.48; p.49, top; p.54-55; p.55,top; p.60, bottom inset; p.60-61; Smith/Zefa, p.72; Hub Willson, p.104, op inset; M.C. Wootton, p.109; p.114, inset; p.115, top; M. Gibson, p.115,bottom; p.125; George Hunter, p.85, top

Holt Studios Intl: p.104, bottom inset

Image Bank: Ron Chapple, p.32-33; Alain Choisnet, p.45, top;

Patrick Eden, p.103, top; Gary Gladstone, p.70, right inset; Tom Knibbs, p.103; Marc Loiseau, p.42-43; Michael Melford, p.211, p.98, center; Terie Rakke, p.20, bottom left, p.90l, inset; Marc Rumantelli, p.45, bottom; Alvis Upitis, p.20, bottom right

International Stock: p.80, Tom Carroll, p.33, bottom

Joy Mining: p.78, top inset, p.79, top, bottom inset

Komatsu: p.21, top; p.71; p. 92; p.93, top & bottom

Krupp Foedertechnik: p.5l, inset, Contents, p.73, top; p.74, center

Lamont, Dan: p.71

Library of Transportation: p.55, bottom; p.9, top, center, bottom

Liebherr: p.47, top; p.64-65; p.68,bottom & inset; p.69; p.106, inset

Marion: p.56

Mejuto, James M.: p.19, top center

NASA: p.120-121; p.120, inset; p.121, inset

New Holland: p.99, top, bottom, center

Network Aspen: p.14, inset; Jeffrey Aaronson, p.14-15; p.15, bottom inset

Newell Industries: p.112

O'Neal, Lamont: p.55, illustration

Odyssey: Robert Frerck, p.11, top right, bottom inset

P&H: p.60; p.63, bottom

Photo Researchers: p.10, bottom; Bill Bachmann, p.46, p.74, top; George Haling, p.114, bottom left; Garry D. McMichael, p.104-105, top; Lee F. Snyder, p.27, center

Photri: p.112-113; p.116, bottom inset; p.116, top inset; p.117, top; p.117, top inset; p.5, bottom inset, Contents, p.121, inset

QA Photos: p.84; p.85, bottom left; p.86, top; p.87, inset; p.88; p.89, top; p.89, center; p.89, bottom

R.G. LeTourneau University: p.28, top right; p.29, top right, top left, bottom right, right inset

Rheinbraun Aktiengesellschaft: p76, top, bottom; p.77

Robbins Co.: p.86, bottom; p.87, bottom

Tony Stone: p.7, bottom; Paul Chesley, p.7, top right; p.11; Stewart Cohen, p.64, inset; p.84, inset; Janet Gill, p.16-17, p.32, top; I.M. House, p.120; David Joel, p.18, right top; H. Richard Johnston, p.84, top inset; Zigy Kaluzny, p.104, top; Mitch Kezar, p.96-97; Andrew Sacks, p.4-5, p.105; Mark Segal, p.36-37; Vince Streano, p.25, top; Jeremy Walker, p.7, bottom right

Tower Cranes of America: p.51, top

UPI/Corbis-Bettman: p.12-13; Underwood & Underwood, p.12l, inset, p.28l, inset, p.48l; Corbis-Bettman, p.39, bottom left; p.70, top, p.71, left inset

Vermeer: p.4, bottom inset, Contents; p.34, top, bottom; p.35, inset

Westlight: p.90, bottom inset; p.23, right; Larry Lee, p.40l

Woodfall Wild Images: p.88; p.106; Adrian Dorst, p.107, bottom; p.108, bottom

YVA/Momatiuk: John Eatcott, p.104, bottom inset